This book belongs to

Stories were specially written for this book by:

Georgina Adams John Adlard Marcia Armitage Frank Arthur Susan Baker Greta Coates Elizabeth Cooper Pamela Dormer Eileen Fauset Eugénie Garner Tytus Huffman Vicky Humpherson Fiona Hunt Edna Hutchings Jill Kevan Harold Lamb Gillian Maxwell Mabel Wilson McIntosh Joyce Upson Freda Ward Ralph Whitlock

The illustrations are by:

Catherine Bradbury Grahame Corbett Sandy Ford Nina Klein Carol Lawson Chris McEwan Jennifer Parsons Laura Potter Brenda Meredith Seymour Ron Stenberg

Published 1976 by
The Hamlyn Publishing Group Limited
London · New York · Sydney · Toronto
Astronaut House, Feltham, Middlesex, England

ISBN 0 600 36568 9

Printed by New Interlitho, Milan, Italy.

Some of the material in this book first appeared in annuals and storybooks published by the Hamlyn Publishing Group between 1963 and 1971.

My Bedtime Storybook

Hamlyn
London · New York
Sydney · Toronto

Contents

The Pink Rabbit

'Oh! What a lovely pink rabbit,' cried Peter when he peeped into the larder and saw the rabbit sitting on a green plate.

Peter thought it looked almost alive, and when he touched the plate he jumped with surprise. The rabbit moved! He pulled the plate closer to make sure. Yes! Just as he thought, the rabbit was shivering.

'It must be too cold for it in the larder,' he thought. 'I will put it in the warm kitchen.'

So he carefully carried the plate over to the kitchen table beside a hot radiator.

But the rabbit wouldn't stop shivering. Every time Peter ran into the room to look at it, it seemed to shiver even more. It looked very sad too. Its ears seemed to be drooping and it almost looked as if it were crying as it sat huddled on the plate.

Peter went outside to play and forgot all about the rabbit. But when he came in for tea he had a terrible shock.

Mummy was in the kitchen looking very puzzled, and mopping up a sticky pink puddle on the table.

'That's very strange,' she was saying, 'I'm sure I remembered to put that jelly in the larder.'

'What jelly?' Peter asked.

'It was a pink rabbit,' she said, 'made from strawberry jelly and cream. I used a special rabbit-shaped mould that Granny gave me. It looked very life-like when it had set. I turned it out on to this grass-green plate. But here is the remains of it, all melted away because of the heat from the radiator. And I was sure I had put it on a cool shelf in the larder. What could have happened?'

'It was my fault,' Peter confessed. 'I thought the rabbit was shivering because it was too cold. So I brought it in here.'

'Oh dear! What a silly thing to do. Now whatever will we have for tea?' Mummy scolded gently.

'Pour some of the runny jelly into a bowl,' Peter suggested. 'I am sure it will taste just as nice. In fact if it had still looked like a rabbit I wouldn't have wanted to eat any. It looked too much like a real live one.'

Nurseryland Dream

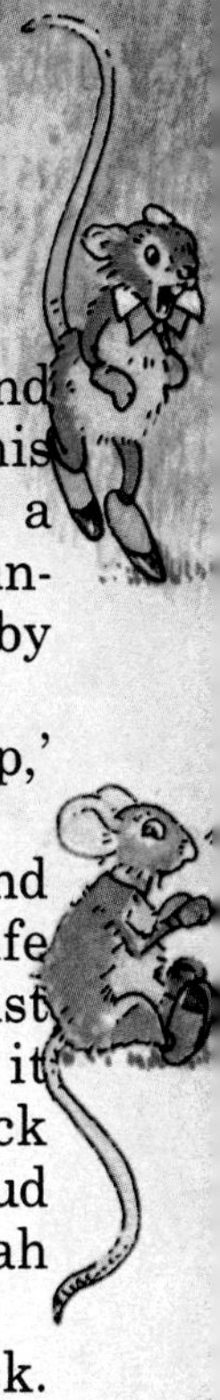

'Tick-tock, tick-tock. Eight o'clock, eight o'clock,' ticked the nursery wall clock furiously. 'It is time you were asleep, Sarah. Tut-tut!'

'"Tick-tock," you mean,' giggled Sarah snuggling underneath the bedclothes with her nursery rhyme book. 'Just one more rhyme and then I'll go to sleep,' she promised. Sleepily she began to read:

'Jack and Jill went up the hill,
To fetch a pail of water;
Jack fell down and broke his crown
And . . .'

Sarah came tumbling after. Thump. Bump. She landed at the bottom of a hill and rolled into a haystack.

'Ouch!' said a little boy dressed in blue. 'You woke me up.' And he began to cry.

'You must be Little Boy Blue,' said Sarah. 'Well, stop crying and go and look after your sheep. They are in the meadow, you know, and your cows are in the corn!'

Sarah clambered out of the haystack and went to look for poor Jack to mend his broken crown. Just as she was passing a farmhouse she saw the farmer's wife running round and round inside, chased by three blind mice.

'Goodness!' said Sarah. 'I had better help,' and she began to chase the mice.

Upstairs and downstairs they ran, in and out of all the rooms, the farmer's wife getting crosser and crosser. Sarah was just about to catch one of the mice when it dashed up a great big grandfather clock standing in the hall. Suddenly, with a loud *dong!* the clock struck one and Sarah awoke with a start.

'Oh,' she said to the nursery wall clock. 'Did you strike one o'clock?'

'Tick-tock. No I did not!' ticked the nursery wall clock impatiently. 'It's *nine* o'clock in the morning and time you were out of bed!'

The Owl Who Needed Glasses

Once, in the middle of a wood, there lived a long-sighted owl. Although Owl could see the stars in the sky at night, and the ants crawling about on the ground when he was sitting in a tree, he could not see what was right in front of his nose. And that made things very difficult for him.

Once he flew into a tree and bruised his beak so badly that he could not hoot for a week. The other animals in the wood were worried about him.

'We must persuade Owl to wear glasses,' said Badger one morning.

Owl was sitting high in a tree above their heads, snoring away.

'Hi there, Owl!' called one of the rabbits. 'Can we have a word with you?'

'Uhu-a-a-a-aaaahmmm,' yawned Owl. His eyes opened for a brief second, and then he fell asleep again.

'It's no use trying to talk to him now,' said Badger. 'We must wait until he's properly awake. We will all meet here at sunset.'

That night the animals gathered together to talk to Owl. Unfortunately Owl had woken early and flown off into the night.

'We must look for him,' said Badger, who was holding a pair of white-rimmed glasses. 'He may be stuck somewhere. Whoever finds him must tell him to hoot loudly three times and then we will all know where to come. Let's go looking now.'

It was one of the rabbits who eventually found Owl. He was talking to an old gnarled tree trunk lying on the ground, saying, 'Wake up, Badger. What are you doing down there?'

'Hullo, Owl,' said Rabbit.

'I'm so glad you've come along,' said Owl, who knew it was Rabbit, because he recognised his voice. 'There seems to be something wrong with Badger. Do you think he is hurt?'

'Of course not, that's a ——' Then Rabbit stopped and said instead, 'Hoot three times, Owl, and the other animals will come.'

Owl obliged and everyone came running, including Badger, of course. Owl peered at him through half-closed eyes.

'You're Badger, aren't you?' he said. Badger said that he was.

'Then who is that down there?' asked Owl, confused.

Badger laughed and propped the white-rimmed glasses over Owl's beak.

'Gracious me!' said Owl, looking through them at the tree trunk. 'Fancy thinking that was Badger.' He looked around. 'Why, I can see all your faces quite clearly. I shall always wear glasses now.'

After that, the only time he bumped into a tree was when he forgot to put the glasses on, and that was not very often.

The Fish

I took a jamjar and my net
To try and catch a fish;
I thought we'd have it for our tea,
Served on a silver dish.
The only fish that I could find
Was small and black, and so
I put him in a goldfish bowl
And hoped that he would grow.
To my surprise he lost his tail
and grew two legs instead.
When next I saw him, Freddy Frog
Was sitting on my bed!

A Bus Ride in the Nursery

Before Jeremy went to bed he always tidied away his toys and put them into the toy cupboard. He put his big motor car and the garage on the floor by the wall, and he put his books in his desk.

One night he was tired as Mummy had allowed him to stay up late, so instead of tidying the nursery, he had left his toys all over the floor.

Long after Jeremy had fallen asleep, the toys started to wake up.

'Where are we? Why aren't we in the cupboard?' asked the rabbit.

'I don't know,' answered Teddy Bear in his growly voice. 'But it isn't too comfortable lying on this hard floor!'

The toys wondered what they could do.

Then Ben, the rubber clown, said, 'We'll play buses with the big red pedal car, like Jeremy does.'

'Oh, goody!' Teddy shrieked, 'I'll be the driver.'

'No you won't. I'm the driver,' argued Spot, the fluffy dog.

Ben, the rubber clown, shouted sternly, 'I shall be the bus driver because it was my idea. You can be the conductor, Teddy. The rest of you can be the passengers.'

Into the driver's seat went Ben, and Teddy put on Jeremy's conductor's hat, which was really much too big for him, and kept falling over his eyes. Spot the dog, Ronnie Rabbit and Panda all climbed aboard.

'Hold very tight, please,' called out Teddy. 'Fares please!'

Round and round the nursery went the car. How it liked pretending to be a bus!

The toys played at buses for a long time, until it started to get light. Then Panda said, 'Shall we go back into the cupboard now? I'm feeling tired.'

'Yes,' Teddy answered. 'That will be a surprise for Jeremy in the morning, won't it? He will find a nice, tidy nursery.'

They walked slowly to the cupboard, because they were all so tired. Panda, who was the tallest, helped them to climb in.

Next morning, after Jeremy had eaten his breakfast, he went into the nursery. What a shock he had! The toys were all in their places in the cupboard.

'How did you get in there?' he asked. But, of course, the toys could not tell him.

The Merry Baker

Bang-bang-bang! Harry was making a new door for his house. 'Hallo, Harry,' said the Merry Baker, as he came down the road with his van. 'Do not work too hard.'

Harry stopped hammering. He felt hungry when he saw the good things in the Baker's van. 'Can I have a currant bun please?' he asked.

'Yes, if you have the right sort of money to pay for it,' said the Merry Baker, laughing. 'I want some planks of wood and some nails.'

Harry thought this was a funny way to pay, but he gave the Merry Baker the planks and the nails, and sat down to eat his currant bun.

Mr Goss next door was working in his garden. 'Can I have a cake please?' he shouted.

'Of course you can,' said the Merry Baker, 'if you have the right kind of money to pay for it. That will be a large bag of grass seed and a load of daffodils.'

Mr Goss thought this was a funny way to pay, but he gave him the grass seed and the daffodils happily enough.

At Rose Cottage Mrs Betts was doing her spring cleaning. 'I want a white loaf, please,' she called.

'Here you are,' said the Merry Baker, 'and to pay for it I should like a bed, a blanket and some kitchen chairs.'

Mrs Betts thought this was a funny way to pay, but she found him a bed, a blanket and some kitchen chairs.

The Merry Baker was very happy. He had sold all his bread and cakes.

He borrowed Harry's hammer, and with the planks and nails he made himself a house. He borrowed Mr Goss's spade and sowed the grass seed and planted the daffodils. Soon he had a lovely garden.

Then he went inside his house and made a room with the chairs, the bed and the blanket. How he sang as he worked!

'Now I have no money,' said the Merry Baker to himself, 'but what a lovely home I have to live in.'

My Magic Carpet

Each night when I should be in bed
I sit upon my rug instead.
I screw my eyes up very tight
And wish and wish with all my might.
Then off we sail above the trees
Across the eery moon-flecked seas
To lands I've never seen before
Where tigers stalk and lions roar.
Lands where nothing can be seen but snow;
Where deserts stretch and palm trees grow;
Where forests are so thick and green
That slithering snakes can lurk unseen.
All these I see as I fly past
Until I turn for home at last.
Then safely into bed I creep.
My travels done, I fall asleep!

The Wiggle Toe Family

After their evening baths, the Wiggles children sat on the mat toasting their fat, pink, freshly-powdered toes in front of the fire. They were all feeling very warm and comfortable.

Mr Wiggles sat looking at their toes and thinking.

Presently he said, 'Now that *is* surprising! No,' he added, 'It's more than surprising. It's *super-surprising!'*

'What is super-surprising?' asked Mrs Wiggles.

'Toes,' replied Mr Wiggles. 'Toes.'

'Toes?' echoed Mrs Wiggles.

Mr Wiggles nodded his head. Then he said, 'Do you know how many toes there are in this room at this moment?'

'No,' said Mrs Wiggles and waited for him to tell her. She was no good at sums, but she was very proud of the clever way Mr Wiggles did them.

'Well,' he began. 'There are two of us and the four children. That's six people. Each of us has two feet and on each foot we have five toes. That means that we have a grand total of *sixty* toes between us. *Sixty* toes in this room!'

'Oh my!' exclaimed Mrs Wiggles. 'That really is a *grand* total of toes in one family.'

When, a little later, she told the children that it was time for bed, their *forty* toes followed Mrs Wiggles's *ten* toes upstairs. That left just the ten toes of Mr Wiggles in front of the fire.

'Hmm,' he muttered aloud. 'Sixty toes are far too many for this small mat. Tomorrow I must buy a larger one.'

And with the happy thought of a brand new brightly-coloured mat in mind, he stretched his legs and wiggled his toes!

The Fat Teddy Bear

Podge was a teddy bear with a very fat tummy indeed.

'Well, what can you expect if you *will* eat all those cream cakes!' Hoppity, the toy rabbit, pointed out.

'But I *like* cream cakes,' Podge protested.

'Eat lettuce instead, like me,' suggested Hoppity.

'And bananas, like me,' said Cheeko, the toy monkey.

'And fish, like me,' purred Tabitha, the fluffy cat.

'Perhaps you are right,' sighed poor Podge.

That afternoon he ate a whole lettuce for tea, though he did not like it at all. For breakfast next morning he ate two bananas, and for lunch he ate some fish. Then he looked at his reflection in the looking glass.

'No. I am *not* any thinner!' he said glumly. 'And what's more, I feel very hungry!'

Podge decided to go for a walk. On the village green he met Tommy, the toy soldier.

'Why do you look so sad, Podge?' he asked him.

'I am too fat!' said Podge. 'I am on a diet.'

'Dieting is no good!' scoffed Tommy. 'Exercise is what you need, Podge. Why not walk right to the top of Hard-to-Climb Hill?'

Hard-to-Climb Hill was very steep, and it took Podge a long time to reach the top. When he did he was out of breath, and his legs ached. He sat down, and in two minutes he was asleep.

He was wakened by his best friend, Bettina, the blue-eyed doll.

'Hello, Bettina,' Podge yawned. 'I was so tired, I fell asleep. It must be all this exercise and dieting.'

'What exercise and dieting?'

'Well, I am too fat, you see.'

'Who says you are too fat?'

Podge looked surprised. 'Don't *you* think I am too fat?'

'Certainly not!' Bettina declared. 'I like you just as you are, Podge! Besides, have you ever heard of a *thin* teddy bear?'

Podge thought hard. 'No,' he said at last.

'Neither have I!' said Bettina. 'Teddy bears are always fat and cuddlesome. That is why everybody loves them. Now come home at once, and have some cream cakes for afternoon tea!'

The Foolish Frog

Ferdinand was a very foolish and stupid frog. He would not listen to all the things his parents tried to teach him.

When he was old enough, Mr and Mrs Frog sent him away to make a home for himself, as all frogs must do at some time.

Ferdinand did not even bother to go very far – he just made his home in some reeds he paddled into on the river bank.

It was a very black night. No moon. No stars.

The wind in the reeds made a frightening *whooooosh*ing noise.

The river, whipped up by the *whooooosh*ing of the wind, made a frightening *sluuuurp*-ing noise. An extra *whoooosh* by the wind and an extra *sluuuurp* from the river and Ferdinand was washed clean out of bed!

It was a miserable, frightened Ferdinand who hopped back to his old home first thing in the morning.

'Please take me back,' he begged. 'I've been such a foolish frog. If only you'll take me back, I'll listen and I'll learn,' Ferdinand promised.

Of course Mr and Mrs Frog took him back and taught him all over again everything a young frog needs to know about building his own home.

Now, Ferdinand has the best, *the very best* home along the river bank, and he built it so that there was no chance of his ever being washed out of bed again!

Naughty Emma Jane

That naughty little Emma Jane!
She hid her mummy's hat again.
She broke a saucer and a cup,
And wouldn't do her laces up.
She tore two pages in her book,
And what a dreadful time she took
In walking down the lane!

That naughty little Emma Jane!
She says, 'I won't be bad again.
Tomorrow I'll be good as gold,
And I'll do everything I'm told.'
But when tomorrow comes, I'm sure
She'll be up to her tricks once more.
She's always just the same!

The River Adventure

Sweet Tooth, Loose Tooth and Long-in-the-Tooth were three little water shrews who lived in the bank of a stream. Every springtime the river overspilled and flooded the meadows, and one morning the water came rushing and gurgling through their front door.

As usual they were not prepared. They had time only to clutch their nightcaps as the brown water swirled into their bedroom. In a moment three little polished brass bedsteads were swept into midstream. They bobbed and spun wildly in the rushing water.

Now water shrews can swim very well, but Sweet Tooth, Loose Tooth and Long-in-the-Tooth were not as young as they used to be, and the water was very rough. So, tucking their sharp noses under the bedclothes, they pretended they were still at home.

Sweet Tooth's teeth chattered with fright, Loose Tooth's teeth chattered with cold, and Long-in-the-Tooth's one tooth provided him with a shrill policeman's whistle.

Suddenly Long-in-the-Tooth shouted, 'Hoist the sails!' Reluctantly the others tied two corners of their bedspreads to their bedposts and held the other two corners fast. Just in time – there was the big river!

'I've never seen the sea,' gasped Sweet Tooth. The wind filled his sail.

'Nor have I,' shrilled Loose Tooth. A wave lifted his raft.

'And I never want to!' whistled Long-in-the-Tooth as the breeze snatched his nightcap from his head.

But after a few miles they got used to being tossed about. They lay back watching the banks race past. Long-in-the-Tooth whistled. The river roared.

Sweet Tooth was sucking a peppermint he had found under his pillow when it suddenly happened. One minute they were sailing smoothly, the next, they were flying upwards through the air.

Tim and Mary had waited on the bridge all morning hoping some treasure would float past. Tim caught the rafts in his fishing net, and they hurried home to look at their catch.

'Only girls' toys,' grumbled Tim, but Mary fetched her smallest dolls and tucked them in the beds.

Sweet Tooth, Loose Tooth and Long-in-the-Tooth escaped unseen. They made a new home in some watercress beds, and they were often heard to boast about their dangerous voyage and how terribly brave they had been!

The Animal Teacher

Helen knew it wasn't cold for the time of year. In fact the sun shone warmly in the little country lane.

So why was that little old lady hopping up and down near the hedge?

'Are you hopping to keep warm?' Helen asked her.

'No, my dear,' the old lady answered. 'I'm teaching baby rabbits to hop.'

Helen looked in the hedge. To her surprise she saw three baby rabbits hopping up and down energetically.

'But rabbits know how to hop!' she exclaimed.

'No,' the lady answered. 'They have to be taught rabbit things just like you're taught people things. Come, I have other pupils waiting.'

Helen followed the old lady down the lane to a lake surrounded by woods.

The lady walked to a tree and parted its leaves. Underneath were three young sparrows in a nest.

'It's time for their chirping lesson,' she said, tapping their nest for attention. Then she began to chirp. The birds chirped back.

'It's young mole's turn next,' the lady said, replacing the leaves. 'He must be taught to dig. Ah, there he is now.'

Helen saw a mole on the ground squinting up at them.

'This sun is too strong for you,' the old lady said bending over, 'so learn to dig deep tunnels – like this.' Her hands dug quickly into the earth. Soon only her feet were sticking out.

The mole began to dig and vanished down its own tunnel.

'Now for my baby bees,' the old lady said, reappearing and shaking off the dirt.

There was a hole in a tree nearby. She put her head in and buzzed. Helen heard a thousand little buzzes answer.

'That's easier than teaching worms to wiggle,' said the old lady, pulling her head back, 'or teaching snakes to crawl.'

Helen laughed. 'Next you'll tell me you teach fishes to swim.'

'How kind of you to remind me,' the old lady replied. 'They must be tired of waiting.'

The last Helen saw, the lady was bobbing up and down in the lake. A school of little fishes bobbed up and down beside her.

Saturday Morning

Where is Mary?
In the dairy
Weighing up the cheese.

Where is Dora?
On the floor
A-scrubbing on her knees.

Where is Bella?
In the cellar
Climbing on the coke.

Where is Mother?
Putting brother
Billy's jeans to soak.

Where is Father?
Masked in lather
Ready for a shave.

Where is Ben? He's
At the Dentist
Trying to be brave.

Where is Pam?
Making jam
Ready for the shelf.

Where is Hugh?
Trying to do
Homework by himself.

Where am I?
I'm up high
In the apple tree.
I read and munch
Till time for lunch,
Then they'll call for me.

The Special Lamppost

Once upon a time there was a lamppost. It was a bright green lamppost, and it stood in a long line with nineteen other lampposts on a promenade by the sea.

But the lamppost wasn't at all happy.

He wanted to be important.

What he really wanted, most of all in the whole world, was to be a lighthouse.

The lighthouse stood like a great stone giant at the edge of the bay, and at night the lamppost could see its beams as it blinked its huge light to warn the boats not to get too close to the rocks.

Then one night it started to rain and the wind began to blow. It blew stronger and stronger. The seagulls took shelter, while far out to sea a ship battled its way through waves that were as high as mountains.

The lamppost could hardly stand up against the storm. He lost his breath and his light blew out, and the promenade was quite dark.

Then suddenly the lamppost saw that a terrible thing had happened.

The lighthouse was in darkness too.

Not a light showed anywhere, and the ship tossed helplessly up and down, drifting every minute nearer and nearer the rocks.

And then the lamppost had an idea.

Here, at last, was his big chance to shine. He heaved and he strained. And then at last, on came his light.

Far out to sea, a huge wave had lifted the ship nearer the rocks. Water was washing over the decks, and the passengers were trying not to get their feet wet.

Then suddenly they saw the tiny light twinkling in the distance.

'Steer clear of the rocks!' shouted the bo'sun, and the captain turned the ship round and headed out to sea.

When the storm was over the passengers on the ship scrambled safely ashore. How surprised they were to find that the light that had saved their lives came from a lamppost on the promenade!

Soon the story of his brave effort had spread all round the town, and the Mayor gave the lamppost a special notice to wear which said: 'Deputy Lighthouse. By Special Appointment'.

And every week the lighthouse keeper visited him to make sure his light was in order, and to give him a special salute.

The Missing Kitten

Lots of animals lived with Don at Dumbledor Farm. There were cows, pigs, sheep, chickens, a pony called Parsnip and a dog called Tumble. There were some cats, too. The cats' names were Tomkin, Mewly, Pan and Fluffles.

Most of the animals lived in the barns, but Fluffles had a cardboard box with a blanket in it under the kitchen table, because she had a family of small kittens. There were four of them, just starting to crawl about.

The biggest of them was black and had long fur. He was a lovely kitten. Don called him Bimkin.

One afternoon Bimkin was missing. All the other kittens were there, but Bimkin had vanished. Mother said, 'I expect Fluffles has taken him over to the barn. Cats often move their kittens from one place to another. They carry them in their mouths.'

Don thought he would see whether Bimkin *was* in the barn. He looked in the cow stalls, and in the pen where Vincent the bull lived when he was at home. Don rolled in the straw and jumped about in the hay and climbed up the ladder to the loft, but he couldn't find Bimkin.

In a room under the loft Mother had broody hens, sitting on eggs. Each hen had an orange box with a straw nest in it. On the straw were fourteen eggs. The hen sat on the eggs for three weeks, and then the baby chicks hatched out of the eggs. Some of the eggs were just hatching.

Don lay on his stomach now and started talking to the hens. Then suddenly he stopped. There, peeping out from under a hen's wing, was a little black furry head.

'Bimkin!' said Don.

He reached out to pick up the kitten, but the hen gave him a little warning peck. Then with her beak she pushed Bimkin back out of sight, under her warm body. She had adopted the little kitten.

When Don ran to tell his mother she said, 'Well, I think we'd better give Fluffles an orange box next to the hens.'

So she did. Then Bimkin sometimes sat with Fluffles in her orange box, and sometimes in the hen's orange box with her new friends, the baby chicks.

Look for other stories about Dumbledor Farm in this book on pages 55, 93 and 138.

The Seagulls' Nest

It was a fine spring day and the young seagull chicks were sitting on the edge of their nest, enjoying the tickling sensation as the breeze ruffled their mottled feathers.

'Let's go down for a swim,' suggested the boldest chick.

'Ooh! It looks an awful long way,' the smallest one complained.

The chicks had only just learnt to fly and hadn't been far from the nest yet.

'Come on! It's easy, follow me!' said the boldest, and dived off the ledge. The others followed, except for the smallest, who hesitated for a few moments.

But when he saw the others down on the water, skimming about, diving and splashing, he couldn't resist following them. Down he went, opening his wings wide to slow himself as he landed on the water.

It certainly was fun. In fact, the smallest gull didn't want to go home, and when the others left, he stayed behind, bobbing on the waves like a cork.

Eventually he began to feel rather lonely and he decided to go home too. Up he flew, spiralling round and round on the strong rush of air that blew up off the water. It made him feel quite dizzy, and he wasn't sure where he was.

And where was his nest? There were hundreds of them in rows on the cliff ledges, and they all looked alike.

Wasn't it near that patch of pinks? But no! A strange, angry mother hissed at him.

Or was it above that wide stony ledge? Wrong again. Those nests were deserted.

He began to cry with a plaintive mewing sound.

'Whee! Whee! Whee-where-are-you?' he called.

Jenny and her mother were sitting on the cliff top eating ice-cream.

'That young seagull sounds just like you did when you couldn't find our new flat,' Jenny's mother said.

Jenny remembered how she used to cry when she looked up from the playground at the huge tower block of flats, and couldn't see which one was their window.

'Look! The mother gull has gone out to fetch him, just like you used to do,' Jane pointed out.

And sure enough, the smallest gull was safely back in his nest at last.

The Whistle

Once upon a time there was a boy who had a new whistle. As he was walking through the wood, it fell out of his pocket. And there it lay.

Soon along came a little rabbit.

'What is this?' he said. 'Does it bite?'

So he went up to it with care, but it did not bite.

Then along came a little green frog.

'What is this?' he asked.

'It does not bite,' said the rabbit.

'Does it jump?' said the frog, and he gave it a push. But it did not jump.

Then along came a little bird.

'What is this?' asked the bird.

'It does not bite,' said the rabbit.

'It does not jump,' said the frog.

'Does it sing?' said the bird, and he listened carefully. But it remained quite silent.

Then along came a hedgehog.

'What is this?' he asked.

'It does not bite,' said the rabbit.

'It does not jump,' said the frog.

'It does not sing,' said the bird.

'Is it good to eat?' said the hedgehog, and he bit it. But it was too hard.

Just then along came the boy, looking for his whistle.

'Here it is!' he shouted, and he picked it up, and blew and blew. 'Wheeeeeeeee!'

The rabbit and the frog and the bird and the hedgehog all ran away as fast as they could, and when they had run a long way they stopped and said:

'So *that* is what it does!'

The River

River, river,
Roaming on,
Shooting sparkles
From the sun.
Laughing shallows,
Silent deep,
Rippling gently,
Rushing steep.
Whispering secrets,
Sighing dreams,
Reflected visions
Parting streams.
Roaming river,
Is it true
That there is no end to you?

Mr Finn's Fruit Stall

'Dear me!' sighed Mr Finn. 'I haven't sold much fruit today.'

He took some left-over fruit from his market stall, put it in his van and drove home.

Underneath the stall, in a box, was a pineapple Mr Finn had forgotten. When it was dark, the pineapple stretched himself and clambered out of the box. He looked up at the stall.

'If I made the stall look nice, people might notice it more,' thought Pineapple.

He searched around the market, and he found some blue tissue paper that had been wrapped around oranges. Under the stationery stall he found a broken crayon, some red paper and a drawing-pin. Under the toy stall he found a yellow balloon that had lost its air. It was on a long orange string. Then he found a green ribbon.

Pineapple was soon making the tissue paper into pretty blue flowers, which he arranged all over the market stall. Then on the piece of paper, Pineapple wrote with the crayon in big letters: MR FINN'S FRUIT STALL. He pinned this to the stall. He wound the green ribbon around a front leg of the stall, and part of the orange string around the other front leg. Then he blew up the balloon. There was still some string on it, so Pineapple tied the balloon to the stall.

Then Pineapple yawned and climbed into his box for a sleep.

When Mr Finn arrived next morning and saw the stall with its red letters, blue flowers, yellow balloon, green ribbon and orange string, he could hardly believe his eyes. He was soon arranging his fruit on the stall, and he took Pineapple from the box and put him in the centre of the fruit. When market visitors saw the stall they came to have a closer look. Then they noticed the fruit and decided to buy some. Soon Mr Finn's stall was very busy.

Mr Finn was very happy, but he said to himself, 'Who decorated my stall so nicely? I wonder who did it.'

Do you know, Mr Finn was almost sure he heard a chuckle come from his pineapple!

Charlie Gnome's Mushrooms

Charlie Gnome jumped out of bed on the wrong side one morning and knocked over his favourite mushroom table. It broke into tiny pieces. He looked sadly at it.

'I might as well fry it for breakfast. It is no use for anything else.'

He had just placed his plate covered with cooked mushrooms down by the fire to keep warm, when a sound like thunder came from the chimney. His kitchen was filled with soot and his breakfast was covered with it.

Charlie danced up and down with rage.

'It's that cat Sam again! I'll teach him to climb all over my roof.'

He was still dancing with fury when the soot cleared and there on the hearth sat a black cat. He was grinning from ear to ear.

Charlie picked up the plate of sooty mushrooms and emptied it all over Sam. 'And there they will stay till you say you are sorry,' said Charlie. 'Now, outside!' And he opened his door to let out a mushroom-covered Sam, still grinning.

Sam found a quiet spot and settled down to clean himself. But he just couldn't. The mushrooms stuck to his fur and the soot tasted so nasty that Sam soon began to feel quite ill. His mistress, Mrs Holly, was a witch and very clever, so Sam hurried home and asked her to help him.

She gave Sam a bath, first in water, then in milk, last of all in dandelion juice. Nothing moved the mushrooms, in fact they seemed to stick faster.

'Perhaps it will wear off,' said Mrs Holly. 'Meanwhile, I think you should go back to Charlie and apologise.'

'I think I will,' said Sam. 'I am beginning to feel a little sorry for walking on Charlie's roof and falling down his chimney.'

As he spoke a small piece of mushroom fell off his back on to the floor.

'Hurrah!' he said. Sam tried to lick more off but the rest were stuck as hard as ever.

Sam ran as fast as he could back to Charlie.

'I really am sorry, Charlie,' he called. 'I promise never to walk on your roof again, or look down your chimney.'

As he said these words he felt a slither on his back, and with a rattle the sooty pieces of mushroom fell on to the lawn.

'I will forgive you, Sam,' he said. 'But if you forget your promise, the mushrooms will come back again.'

They walked away from the lawn towards the house, and Sam turned to go through the gate.

'Why, Charlie,' he called. 'Look at the lawn!'

It was covered with a fine crop of mushrooms, large and small.

As fast as Charlie picked the mushrooms more grew in their place. He was able to have mushroom parties for all his friends and, of course, he always asked Sam.

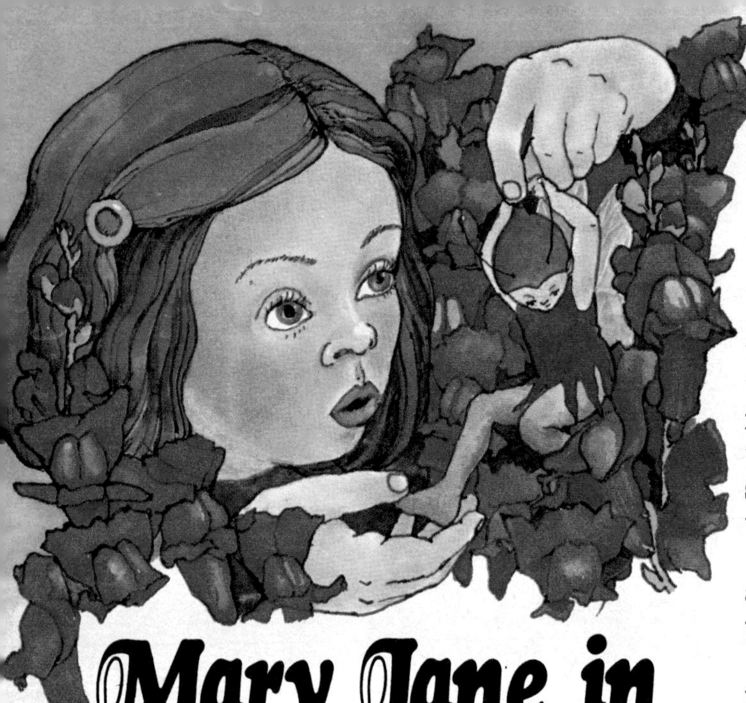

Mary Jane in Fairyland

Mary Jane walked along the garden path, looking at the flowers. Suddenly she heard a tiny, tinkly voice crying, 'Let me out! Oooo, help! Let me out!'

Mary Jane looked all around but could see nothing. She pushed aside some of the flowers to see across the lawn and there, right near her hand, was a fairy's head, peeping out of a snapdragon. The fairy, whose name was Twink, had crept in while she was playing hide-and-seek, and couldn't get out again.

So Mary Jane squeezed open the flower and took Twink out. Then she dusted the yellow pollen off the fairy and sat her on the lawn.

'Oh, thank you,' said Twink. As you have been so kind, would you like to come to Fairyland?'

'Yes, please,' said Mary Jane.

At the bottom of the garden was a huge old tree stump. Twink told Mary Jane to stand on the tree stump and recite the magic rhyme:

'Little gnomes and dwarfs and elves,
Run away and hide yourselves.
Fairy, take me by the hand
And fly with me to Fairyland.'

As she finished the rhyme, the garden vanished, and Mary Jane and Twink were walking through a silvery wood. Another fairy with a wand came to meet them and took them to the fairy palace. There they sat on red cushions and ate blue ice-cream with two goblins and a horse that could talk.

'It is time for you to go,' said Twink, after a while. 'Next time you come you shall meet the Fairy Queen.'

Soon Mary Jane found herself back in the garden. She thought she had been in Fairyland all afternoon, but when she went indoors her mother said, 'Go back and play in the garden, Mary Jane. You have only been in the garden for five minutes.'

So then Mary Jane knew that fairy time was quite different from the time we tell from our clocks and watches. She knew that she would be able to go to Fairyland whenever she wished, and no one would notice she had gone.

Look out for other Mary Jane stories in this book on pages 66 and 119.

The Troubadour and the Dragon

Once there was a troubadour who used to sing for his supper. One day, he saw an old magician trapped in a tree by a fiery dragon, but when he tried to help him, the dragon chased the troubadour into the tree too. Then the magician told him that he had turned his cat into a dragon by mistake, and it was angry.

The troubadour sang sweet songs to soothe the dragon – and it fell asleep! The magician was so pleased, he put a spell on the troubadour's mandolin and then ran away. But when the troubadour tried to run away too, the dragon woke up. He was now a happy dragon, and he liked the troubadour's enchanted music and would not leave him.

So the troubadour took the dragon with him to the next town, but although he was a nice dragon, people were too frightened to hear his songs. The troubadour and the dragon soon became very hungry and unhappy.

But one poor old woman did not run away. She offered the troubadour a dry loaf of bread and begged him to sing a song. Then something happened! The woman turned into a princess. She told him a witch had put a spell on her which only a young man who sang could break.

The princess asked the troubadour if he would be her prince. He agreed happily, so they were married. Then they fixed a cart to the dragon and set off to the princess's castle, where they lived happily ever after.

Shoe

It appears that today
I can find just one shoe.
What does one do
With only one shoe?

When last seen together
They stood on the shelf.
Perhaps one is taking
A walk by itself.

Sweet, Juicy Lemons

Bulmer and Wilmer were two little bears, and like most bears they loved climbing trees and eating sweet things. But they didn't like school: all those numbers and letters were so confusing.

One day their mother promised them a special new treat for tea – sweet, juicy melon.

'Go down to the greengrocer and buy a large ripe yellow one. Here is some money,' she said, 'and please buy me six lemons as well.'

Off went Bulmer and Wilmer, reciting, 'One melon and six lemons . . .' all the way. Bulmer carried the shopping bag and Wilmer held the purse.

The shop was rather busy, but all the fruit and vegetables were arranged in trays outside, neatly labelled with names and price tags.

When it was his turn, Bulmer quickly pointed at the bright yellow fruit and said, 'One of those and six of those, please.'

Wilmer paid, counted the change and they set off home.

Have you ever tried to carry six footballs in a bag? It is extremely difficult. The bag keeps banging your knees, you can't see where you are going, and the top ball keeps rolling off.

And this is what happened to Bulmer and Wilmer, because those silly little bears had made a mistake. They had bought one lemon and six melons because they didn't know their letters properly and had mixed up L and M!

When they got home their mother was busy upstairs, and she called down to them.

'So you're back at last. You must be very hungry. Help yourselves to a slice of melon.'

Bulmer and Wilmer were eager to try this treat after all their trouble. They chopped their 'melon' into four pieces and each took a bite.

'Ugh!'

'Aah!'

They both shrieked, clenching their teeth and screwing up their noses. Their eyes streamed with tears and they coughed and spluttered.

Their mother hurried in to see what was the matter.

'Why are you eating that lemon?' she asked. 'It must be terribly sour. Now why don't you try a slice of melon instead? It's delicious.'

Bulmer and Wilmer looked at the large yellow fruit, ten times larger than their lemon, and they burst out laughing.

Bouncing Ball

Down the empty road came the big rubber ball. As far as Mr Potter the policeman could see there was nobody bouncing it, so whatever could be going on? He began to run after it down the hill, but he could not catch it. Bounce-bounce-bounce it went – on and on.

Old Mrs Dillymop looked over her garden wall just as the ball bounced by. 'My, my,' she cried in great surprise, 'I never saw such a thing before,' and she began to run. She ran along after the ball, with Mr Potter running along behind her.

The ball bounced past the school where the children were just coming out to play. They all ran to the gate and watched the ball go past, followed by Mrs Dillymop and Mr Potter.

'Stop please, and tell us what that ball is doing, bouncing along all by itself,' they cried. But the ball kept bouncing and the runners kept running, so the children came out of the gate and joined the procession.

A little further down the road they met Mr Ratatat the postman on his bicycle. Mrs Dillymop and Mr Potter were very tired and they called to him, 'Please, Mr Ratatat, could you catch the ball on your bicycle?'

So Mr Ratatat set off after the ball, and Mrs Dillymop and Mr Potter sat down to rest, but the children went on running.

When the ball reached the village green, it bounced across the grass and into the pond. Mr Ratatat took a long stick and pulled the ball to the edge. When he picked it up he found it had a split in one side. He pushed his hand into the split, and there inside was the answer to the ball that bounced by itself. He took his hand out and opened it on to the grass, and with a cheery croak of thanks, away hopped a large frog!

The King Who Lost His Voice

King Filador was a bossy king. He loved shouting to his servants. He loved ordering his army about. And he loved yelling at his people.

In fact Filador loved bossing everybody – that is, everybody but his little court jester. It was useless to shout at him. The jester just covered his ears and went to sleep.

Now today the King was bellowing at his people. He stood on the palace balcony, the jester behind him. The people were packed in the courtyard below.

'You must work harder!' Filador shouted.

'You must work longer!' Filador yelled.

'And you must save more!' Filador screamed at the top of his voice.

And the people in the courtyard below? They were tired. They were bored. They shuffled from one foot to the other and looked glum.

Suddenly the King's voice stopped.

Filador grasped the balcony railing. He tried to speak. Only a hoarse croak came out of his mouth!

'I've lost my voice,' he whispered to the jester. 'Help!'

'I'll copy your voice,' the jester whispered back. 'Move your lips in time to my words.'

To the people below the King seemed to start speaking again. But what he said wasn't the same as before – not at all!

He cracked jokes. The crowd laughed.

He told funny stories. The crowd roared.

He sang rollicking songs. The crowd joined in.

It was the King's most successful day!

'How nice to hear jokes,' some people said as they left the courtyard with a smile.

'And how nice to sing songs and listen to funny stories,' others joined in with a merry laugh.

And the King? He was amazed. It was long since he'd seen happy faces.

'Thank you,' he whispered to the court jester. 'Teach me more jokes and stories. Once I've found my voice, I'll talk to my people in future. I will never shout again.'

The Sunshine Umbrellas

Once a wizard lived in a very wet country. It rained almost day and night there.

Many people came to the wizard's house under their umbrellas. They asked for spells to take the rain away and make the sun shine brightly.

But the wizard was only a small wizard. 'I can only do small spells,' he said sadly.

'Hmmph!' the people sniffed. 'We wonder whether you are a real wizard at all. Look at our colds. Look how pale we are. Get busy and help us!' Then they stomped out in the rain under their umbrellas.

The wizard watched them through the window. This was really serious. He might lose his job!

'I can't blow clouds away,' he thought. 'I can't bring the sun out. What can I do?'

He looked at his umbrellas in the corner of the room. There was one for each day of the week. Suddenly he had an idea.

He walked over and picked up Monday's. He opened it and looked up into it. He tilted it back and forth.

'Hmmmm,' he thought. Then he took it over to his magic work bench.

People outside his house saw blue and white flashes in his window. Puffs of green and red smoke shot out of his chimney.

Then his door opened, and the wizard shouted, 'People, come in one by one with your umbrellas. You'll see I'm a real wizard after all.'

One by one the people folded their umbrellas and stepped into the wizard's house. And one by one they stepped out of his house and into the rain. They opened their umbrellas.

Great rays of warm sunshine shone down from inside their umbrellas. Great beams of yellow light bathed them from head to foot.

The people loved their sunshine umbrellas. They took off their hats and coats and rolled up their sleeves.

Then they sat on park benches under their sunshine umbrellas and got more and more tanned. They even stopped sniffing.

And through the rain the wizard heard, 'Three cheers for our wonderful wizard! Hip, Hip, Hooray!'

Hum and Bubble Song

One day, Algie Alligator yawned. It was such a *big* yawn that Hetty Hummingbird fell right into his mouth, and when Algie Alligator looked round to see where she was, she was nowhere to be found.

'That's very strange,' murmured Algie. 'She's most probably playing a trick on me.' So he looked backwards down his long scaly tail but Hetty was not there. Then he pushed his long nose into the rushes by the side of the river but she was not there either.

'I wonder where she could have gone to,' murmured Algie. He was just about to close his eyes and have a little nap when he found himself humming.

'Goodness me,' declared Algie, waking up very fast indeed, 'I've never been able to hum before in my life. In fact, I was just saying to Hetty Hummingbird how very pleasant it would have been if we could have hummed duets together,' and Algie hummed quite a long hum to himself.

But after a little while Algie got rather tired of humming to himself, so he gave a great *big* yawn and closed his eyes. He had hardly closed them before he felt a furious pecking on his nose, and there was Hetty Hummingbird sitting on the end of his long nose and looking very cross indeed.

'You are the rudest alligator I've ever known,' she was saying. 'Why don't you tell somebody when you are going to yawn? I fell in!' she declared.

Algie frowned. 'Was that your hum or my hum that I was humming just now?' he asked.

Hetty ruffled her tail. 'My hum, of course,' she said. 'You know very well you can't hum at all.'

A great big tear dropped from Algie's eye. 'I thought it was me,' he replied. 'I've always wanted to hum a little song to myself, and I really thought I'd done it at

Hetty was so sorry for Algie that she felt she just had to do something to make him happy. 'I know,' she said, 'you blow bubbles and I'll do a little hum, and let's put it together and see how it sounds.'

So Hetty hummed a pretty little tune that exactly fitted the rhythm of Algie's bubbles, and ever since then Algie has been quite content to blow bubbles. But he always turns his head away when he yawns just in case Hetty should fall in again.

Little Black Bear

The sunbeams danced to the back of the cave and tickled the nose of Little Black Bear. His nose twitched and very slowly he opened his two sleepy eyes and looked around him.

Beside him lay Mother Bear, still fast asleep. Little Black Bear shut his eyes again and curled up into a furry ball. But it was no use – he could not go back to sleep.

'I am not the least bit sleepy,' thought the little bear. 'Perhaps a walk will help me.'

He tiptoed out of the cave and wandered off through the forest, ready for a long walk.

'Hello,' called a blackbird, 'shouldn't you be asleep just now?'

'I was,' answered the little bear, 'but the sun woke me up and I can't go back to sleep again. I just do not know what I should do.'

'Why don't you climb the tree and let the wind rock you to sleep,' chirruped the blackbird.

So Little Black Bear began to climb the tree, and was edging his way along a branch when suddenly there was a loud crack. It gave him such a fright!

'Whoops!' he yelled as he and the branch came tumbling down. Luckily, he landed in a patch of snow.

'What is all the noise about?' asked a bad-tempered voice. It was Owl and he was not pleased at being woken so early in the day.

'Little Black Bear can't sleep,' said the blackbird. 'I was trying to help him.'

'I am not surprised,' said the owl very crossly. 'Why should he want to sleep on such a beautiful spring day?'

'It *is* spring!' sang the blackbird as he began to gather twigs for his nest, high up in a fir tree. 'That's why you could not sleep!'

But Little Black Bear was already hurrying home to wake his mother for it was spring and he was very, very hungry.

The Turtles

A paddling turtle in a pool,
Green waving weed below,
His aimless strokes stir ripples cool,
And bubbles rise and go.

With sudden gush and bubbling burst
Frothed water creams the brink;
Wide ripples spread their patterned rings.
I see the turtle sink
Through mists of grey-green watery tide,
To join a friend the other side.

They blink and laze with drowsy gaze;
One last limp stir, one shutting eye,
Then all is still where two stones lie.
Two patterned shells of turtle tweed
Are dappled by the whispering weed.

The Missing Bus

'Come along, children,' exclaimed Mummy, as she hurried to the railway station, 'we must not miss the train to Granny.'

Tessa and Tony, running along at her side, were very excited because they were going to spend a week in the country at Pear Tree Cottage.

In the train they gazed out of the window at pretty red-roofed cottages flashing by, fields full of cows and sheep, and sparkling streams which wound away through woodland.

Presently the train arrived at Henley Halt. Mummy lifted out the suitcases and off they went to catch the local bus to Lilac Lane where Granny lived.

Oh dear, oh dear! The train must have been late arriving because the bus had already gone and there was not another until tomorrow!

'Oh well, we shall just have to walk,' sighed Mummy, as the three set off down the dusty road in the hot sun. They had not gone far before a great hay wagon came rumbling along behind.

'Jump up in the hedge to let it pass, children,' said Mummy. The lane was very narrow.

The wagon did not pass. It came to a halt and the cheery, rosy-faced farmer who was driving it asked, 'Where are you making for?'

When he heard he said, 'Well, ma'am, if you and the two young ones care for a lift, jump up alongside of me. I'll be pleased for the company.'

The children could scarcely believe their ears! They lost no time in scrambling up beside the kindly farmer, who made room for the suitcases and then helped Mummy up. Then off they all jogged down the lane on the sweet-smelling hay wagon beside the jolly farmer, enjoying the nicest ride they had ever had.

And what an adventure it was to tell Granny about when they arrived!

Belinda's Birthday

It was Belinda's sixth birthday, and Mummy and Daddy had given her a parcel. It was very small. Belinda unwrapped it and inside was a tiny yellow duster with red stitches around the edge.

She thanked Mummy and Daddy, but she couldn't help feeling rather disappointed.

'For my first birthday,' thought Belinda, 'I had a Teddy, and for my second, a doll. For my third, I had a doll's pram, and for my fourth, a doll's house. For my fifth I had a dress, and now, on my sixth birthday – just a duster.'

Daddy went to work and Mummy was busy in the kitchen, and as there was nothing else to do, Belinda started to use her duster.

'Dusting isn't a very exciting thing to do,' she sighed.

First, she dusted the table and as she moved the fruit bowl to dust under it, there she saw a neatly-folded hair-ribbon!

'It's just the colour to match my dress,' she said.

She used the ribbon to tie her hair into a pony-tail. Then, as Belinda dusted the four chairs around the table, she found a parcel on each seat. There was a colouring book on one, some crayons on another, a purse with her name on it on the third, and a little hair-brush on the fourth.

On the sideboard she found a pair of doll's shoes just the size for her doll, and on the television a tiny ring with a glass stone. The ring fitted Belinda perfectly. As she watched it sparkle, Mummy came into the room smiling.

'All those things are for you, Belinda,' she said. 'I hid them so you could have fun finding them. While you were dusting I was busy in the kitchen.'

She showed Belinda a lovely big birthday cake she had been icing. It had six candles on it.

Belinda was very happy.

'The dusting kept me busy while you made this surprise for me!' laughed Belinda. 'What a good idea, Mummy, and what a lovely birthday this is!'

Terry Truck

Terry Truck was bright green. Mr Tring the builder used him every day to carry things on his building site. But soon Terry became very muddy and dented and his engine started to rattle.

'It's no good,' sighed Mr Tring one day. 'I shall have to dump this truck.'

Terry gasped in alarm. Whatever was going to happen now?

He soon found out, for he was driven down to the scrap yard and sold to the dealer for spare parts. Terry stood sadly in the rain for days, getting rustier and more uncomfortable all the time.

An old motorbike standing nearby said at last, 'It's awful isn't it? I've been here for weeks, and I suppose I shall end up in pieces.'

'Is that what happens?' asked Terry, horrified.

'Oh yes,' said the bike. 'We old ones take up too much space, so we have to go.'

'Oh dear,' wailed Terry, 'I don't want to be broken up.'

Next day the dealer sorted out all the cars and vans to be broken up, and to Terry's dismay he was one of them.

'You are off tomorrow then?' said the bike. 'He always misses me stuck here in the corner. Well, cheerio Terry! Nice to have met you.'

Terry frowned. It didn't seem fair. Surely he could still be some use if only someone would mend him.

Later that afternoon a man was walking round the yard looking at all the old cars. Suddenly he stopped in front of Terry.

'Why, you are just what I need,' he said, looking under the bonnet. Then he went to find the dealer.

Terry was attached to a tow-truck and whisked off along the road. At last they pulled up outside a big house. The man ran up the steps shouting, 'I've bought one. Come and see. It's just right for our tents when we go camping.' The door flew open

and dozens of small children streamed out and climbed all over Terry in glee.

The man soon mended Terry and painted him a beautiful red. The little truck was so proud, for he soon found that the big house was home to boys and girls who had no mothers or fathers. The kind man and his wife looked after them and loved them all. They had great fun camping in the summer, and Terry thought he was the luckiest truck in the world to have so many friends.

Pillarbox Puzzle

Hoppo the Hare found a knot in his hankie. 'To remind me of something – but what?' he wondered. 'To send Granny Hare a packet of peppermints, perhaps?'

He wrapped the packet in brown paper and bounded off to post his parcel.

'How handy!' whooped Hoppo. The parcel was just flat enough to pass through the slit – thud!

'Owwww!' howled the pillarbox.

Hoppo leapt back in alarm. A talking pillarbox! Then he heard the sound of rustling paper and a voice boomed, 'Ah! My favourite sweets!' There was a crunching, munching noise, and a strong smell of peppermints.

Hoppo was furious! He rushed off to fetch Policeman Mole. 'That new pillarbox has eaten Granny's peppermints!' he cried.

'Which new pillarbox?' asked P.C. Mole.

'That one!' Hoppo pointed to the corner of the lane – but the pillarbox had vanished!

'Up to your tricks again, my lad?' grunted Policeman Mole crossly. Hoppo dashed round the corner – and there was the pillarbox standing quite still.

'It moved!' howled Hoppo.

'Pillarboxes do not move!' frowned P.C. Mole. But at that very moment, the pillarbox did move! It began to trundle down the lane, much to P.C. Mole's surprise.

'See!' crowed Hoppo. Policeman Mole and Hoppo rushed after the runaway pillarbox and threw themselves on it. It toppled over – and someone crawled out through the bottom. It was Basil Badger!

'Basil!' gurgled Hoppo. 'Why are you pretending to be a pillarbox!'

'Because I am on my way to Rabbit's fancy dress party and this is my costume,' puffed Basil.

'Oh dear! That's why I tied a knot in my handkerchief! To remind me to go to the party,' wailed Hoppo. 'And now I have no costume to wear!' Hoppo's ears drooped sadly.

'I'll lend you my helmet, and you can go as a policeman,' said kind P.C. Mole. 'But don't let it happen again, Hoppo, my lad!'

Grandpa's Hat

Bobby was staying with his grandparents. It was a nice spring day and Bobby was helping in the garden. Grandpa was wearing his gardening hat, an old floppy straw one, which Grandma said was a disgrace and should be thrown away.

'Nonsense,' Grandpa used to say. 'It's very comfortable. I like it.'

Swish-swish! The lawn-mower whizzed over the lawn. It was hot work and Grandpa took off his hat to wipe his brow. Then he rested it on a branch of the old apple tree and went on working.

After a while Grandma called them to say that tea was ready and they went indoors. Some time later Grandpa suddenly remembered his hat. 'Fetch it for me, there's a good boy,' he said, and Bobby went running down the garden.

A minute later he was back again. 'Oh, Grandpa, come quickly,' he cried. 'Your hat is full of grass and stuff.'

They walked down to the apple tree to see what it was all about and there, sitting on the brim of Grandpa's gardening hat, was a cheeky little robin, busily arranging the straw inside to make a nest.

'Sssh,' said Grandpa. 'We mustn't disturb him at work.'

'At last, a real use for your old gardening hat,' laughed Grandma.

And do you know, the next time Bobby went to see his grandparents he peeked carefully inside the gardening hat nest, and there were five little white eggs, all speckled with red.

Centipede

The centipede was happy quite,
Until the toad in fun
Said, 'Pray which leg goes after which?'
Which worked his mind to such a pitch
He lay distracted in a ditch
Considering how to run.

Ernest Does a Good Deed

Ernest was an elephant and he lived in the zoo. He had lots of friends and loved to make people happy.

One fine sunny afternoon, just before Ernest was to have his feed of hay and apples, there was a commotion outside the elephant house.

'What on earth is all that noise?' said the zoo keeper to himself. 'I had better go and see.' And off he went. Ernest, being a very inquisitive elephant, naturally followed.

Outside there were lots of people gathering around, and Ernest could hear somebody saying, 'Oh dear, they will all go hungry,' and 'That fish will go off if it is not delivered to them soon.'

As he moved closer to the crowd he could see what had happened. The big lorry which delivered the food to all the animals had broken down. The two back wheels had broken off completely and the back of the lorry had sunk deep into the road.

Ernest was really worried, so he began to think. He thought and thought until at last he had an idea. He boldly marched up to the broken lorry, quickly got down on his front legs, and tunnelled his long trunk underneath the back axle of the lorry.

'Come on Ernie, my boy,' said the zoo keeper excitedly. Soon the entire crowd was shouting to encourage Ernest. Between shouts of 'Clever boy,' and 'Lift it up now,' Ernest managed to raise the back of the lorry off the ground. Then he pushed it along with his massive body as though it were a wheelbarrow.

The crowd cheered and clapped, and the zoo keeper was very proud of Ernest. The animals all had their dinner and Ernest had extra apples that day.

Silly Milly

'Ooh! Isn't it *super*!' cried Billy, looking up at his toy aeroplane flying in the air above the field.

His sister Milly watched open-mouthed. 'I should like to make it fly,' she thought.

Her chance came a few minutes later when Billy, tiring of plane-launching, ran over to the horse-chestnut trees to look for conkers. Milly picked up the abandoned aeroplane and launched it as she had seen Billy do. She trembled with excitement as she watched it fly higher and higher.

'What are you doing, Milly?' cried Billy, seeing his aeroplane sailing through the air. 'I told you not to touch it, you naughty girl!'

He started to run across the field towards his sister. A moment later the aeroplane flew low over the privet hedge at the end of their garden and vanished from sight.

The children dashed through the gateway into the garden, but the aeroplane was nowhere to be seen. And although they searched and searched, Billy and Milly eventually had to give up and go indoors for tea.

Milly couldn't sleep that night. Brother Billy hadn't even said 'Good night' to her, and she wished she'd never played with the aeroplane.

As she stood staring tearfully out of her little bedroom window, she saw something which startled her. Out there, in the paddling pool, was a big silver ball.

In a flash Milly was racing downstairs, out of the back door and across the lawn.

Then, *splash!* In her eagerness to reach the silver ball, Milly overbalanced at the edge of the pool and fell in. Her cries soon brought Daddy and Mummy and Billy to the pool.

'Silly Milly!' Daddy chided her when she told them about the big silver ball she had seen. 'What you saw was the reflection of the moon on the water!'

'Ha, ha!' laughed Billy. 'You came to find the moonlight!'

'Yes,' said his sister with a smile, 'but I've found something else. Look!'

As she drew her hand up out of the shallow water in the pool, Billy saw that she was holding his lost aeroplane!

'I wasn't so silly after all,' said Milly.

Otto and the Black Cloud

Otto the hunter had not caught anything for weeks. There were no monsters to fight, dragons to tame nor thieves to track down. Life was very hard thought Otto, who earned his living by hunting. He decided to see the world, and with his bow over his shoulder and arrows at his belt he set off on his travels.

One morning he came to a high mountain. 'The first country I see from the top of that mountain is where I shall stay awhile,' he thought. Otto was tired when he reached the top. All he could do was rest.

When at last he could look around, Otto was very disappointed. The most miserable countryside lay beneath him. The grass was dead, the trees drooped, and there wasn't a flower to be seen. And a huge black cloud hung over the nearby city.

Otto made his way slowly down the other side of the mountain. At the bottom he saw an old man looking up at the cloud.

'Is it going to rain?' asked Otto politely.

'I wish it would,' said the old man. 'There hasn't been rain or sun since the Green Witch sent the black cloud. Soon, the land will be dead and the people with it.'

'How awful,' said Otto. 'Why did the witch send the cloud?'

'The King banished her from the kingdom,' said the man. 'It was brave of him but very foolish.'

Otto looked at the cloud. It was very low. He fixed an arrow into his bow and fired upwards into the cloud. A drop of water fell on his hand. Then a lot more drops. It was raining!

As the cloud emptied it shrank and shrank until it disappeared and a watery sun came out. People ran from their houses shouting with astonishment.

The King came from the palace demanding to know who had broken the curse. Otto explained what he had done. The King was so delighted that he invited Otto to live in the palace and made him a knight.

The Kite

When the wind blows
Up the kite goes,
Whisking and prancing,
Frisking and dancing
High, high in the sky!
Lovely green kite, like a big leaf swirling,
Twirling and whirling
High, high in the sky!

When the wind drops
Down the kite flops,
Wheeling and shifting,
Reeling and drifting
Down, down to the ground!
Lovely green kite, like a big leaf dipping,
Flipping and slipping
Down, down to the ground!

Salty Water in Tingalee Town

Tingalee town was flooded! It started with a trickle of salty water down the mountain. Now it was a great river through the town. Business was impossible. Everyone was wet and felt miserable.

Then the mayor called a meeting.

'Who'll stop the flood?' he asked. 'Who'll save Tingalee?'

The town beggar arose, his pack on his back.

'I will, Your Honour,' he said. 'Tingalee's been good to me. I'll save it.'

The beggar swam to the library. There he looked up old tales and legends.

Then he waded to the shops. He filled his pack with games, books and model-building kits.

Finally he went to the mountain where the river came down. Taking a deep breath he began to climb, following the salty river's path.

Up he went – over great rocks, past huge forests, through deep valleys – until he came to the clouds.

With outstretched hands he felt his way through the clouds. Then he was in sunshine on the mountain top.

And there, sitting on the mountain's peak, was a huge giant.

The giant was crying. Big salty tears poured down his cheeks. They formed the river that flowed down the mountain.

'Just as I thought,' the beggar laughed. 'And just as the books said.'

The giant stopped crying. He looked down, surprised.

'You're the first person I've seen in years!' he exclaimed happily. 'People don't walk over the mountains now. It's so lonely with no one to see and nothing to do.'

'Everyone travels by car and aeroplane instead,' the beggar answered. But I have brought you some things to cheer you up.

He poured out books, games and building kits from his pack.

Then for days he and the giant played together.

The giant was so interested he stopped crying. And when the beggar finally left, the giant didn't even notice – he was too busy reading and building models.

Now down in Tingalee town the beggar is a hero.

And whenever there is the slightest trickle of salty water from the mountain, the beggar packs his bag with books and games to keep the giant happy.

The Carpet Maker

Once upon a time, in a far-off land, there lived a man who made carpets. He used the softest and the most brightly-coloured wool he could buy, and he made each carpet so carefully that it took him eighteen weeks to make just one. Ali was a happy man, but it was not often that he had a finished carpet to sell, and so he was always poor.

One day another carpet maker moved into the shop next to his. Ben Hadid, the new carpet maker, said, 'What a foolish man you are. Be like me, buy the cheapest wool, make your carpets quickly. Then you will sell more and become as rich as I am.'

'I would rather make one carpet that is truly beautiful,' Ali would reply, 'than make ten that are ugly.'

One morning, as Ali was putting the finishing touches to his latest carpet, there was a clamour at the far end of the street.

Ben Hadid went to see what was happening. What he saw made him run back to his shop in great excitement.

'My greatest day has come,' he gasped, and he dragged out all his finished carpets and laid them on the ground in front of his shop. 'The Caliph has come to the market to buy a new carpet. He is sure to buy one of mine.'

Ali said nothing. He had just finished his carpet when the Caliph stopped outside Ben Hadid's shop.

The Caliph turned over the corner of one of Ben Hadid's carpets to take a closer look.

'This isn't finished properly,' he said, pulling at a loose end. 'It will fall to pieces.'

He rubbed the wool between his fingers to feel its texture.

'Too harsh,' he said. 'That would blister my feet.'

He stepped back so that he could see the design on the front of the carpet. He shook his head.

'The colours are wrong. The design is ugly.'

Ben Hadid was most upset.

And then the Caliph saw the carpet Ali had just finished.

'Hmmm,' he said, looking at it carefully. 'This one is properly finished.' Then he felt the wool between his fingers. 'This will never blister my feet. And what a beautiful pattern. How well the colours are matched. I will buy this one.'

How proud Ali felt!

When the Caliph's servants had taken the carpet to the palace, Ben Hadid turned to Ali and asked humbly, 'Will you help me to become as good a carpet maker as yourself?'

And, of course, kind Ali said he would.

William's Nine Lives

Once upon a time there was a mother cat who told her kitten, 'You have only nine lives.'

'What does that mean?' asked William, the kitten.

'Every time you do a silly thing you will lose a life,' said his mother. 'So be very careful to keep your ninth life, or you will never grow into a wise old cat.'

William climbed on to the window-sill.

Old Grandfather Jones was dozing by the window in the hot sun.

'Miaow!' squealed William in his ear.

'Little nuisance!' shouted Grandfather, shaking his fist at William who went flying through the window and landed in a holly bush.

'Now I've only eight left!' whimpered William.

He went in the meadow and saw a frog hopping along through the grass.

Hoppity plop! went the frog into the stream.

Hoppity splash! went William before he could stop. Down he sank. He bobbed up and down until the stream washed him on to a stone.

That left seven lives.

Thirsty William stuck his head into a jug of milk on the larder floor. Silly William found he could not get his head out again. Frightened William bumped around until the jug broke.

That left six.

Hungry William found a fish-head. Greedy William ate it. It was a very big fish-head which soon stuck in his throat. He choked and choked and then he swallowed it.

That left five.

Tired William strolled into the lane and fell asleep in a warm patch of sun. Round the corner rattled the baker's van. There was a dreadful screeching of brakes as it pulled up suddenly with its front wheel against William's whiskers.

That left four.

William went walking and found a large, furry tail sticking out from behind a garden gate. Naughty William jumped on it and bit it.

'Owwww!' yowled the tail, and over the gate leapt an enormous dog.

Terrified William scrambled up a tree and clung to a branch.

That left three lives.

When the dog went home, William began to stalk a bird on the branch.

'Got you!' squealed William, and pounced.

Away flew the bird, and crack! went the branch. Down fell William, bouncing on the ground.

That left two.

William went exploring in the dustbin. While he was busy inside someone banged down the lid.

'Oh, help!' mewed William.

But no one heard, and he spent a miserable night sleeping on potato peelings and egg-shells.

Next morning the dustmen came and desperate William scrabbled his way out into a puddle.

And that was how William lost eight lives.

Which is why he became sensible William, and looked after his ninth life very carefully indeed after that.

The Magic Horseshoes

When Johnnie and Jane had both gone to bed, all the toys in the playroom began to chatter with excitement. Timothy Tiger and Dobbin, the horse-on-wheels, were running a race.

'I do wish Dobbin could win!' whispered Della the Dutch Doll to Ernest Elephant.

None of the toys liked Timothy Tiger very much. His claws were too sharp! But Dobbin was a very kind-hearted horse, and he gave them lots of rides.

Perry the Policeman was in charge of the race. He set up the winning-post at the other side of the playroom. The winning-post was really a metal signal from Johnnie's railway set.

'Where are my wheels?' neighed Dobbin angrily. 'Someone has stolen my wheels.'

Timothy Tiger looked up at the ceiling, just as though the last thing he could possibly know was who had hidden Dobbin's wooden wheels.

'It isn't fair!' said Della indignantly. 'Dobbin can't race without his wheels!'

But Perry was a very clever policeman. He couldn't find the wheels, but he remembered something else. He marched straight up to Johnnie's desk and lifted down a wooden box. Perry opened it up and took out four little horseshoes.

'I don't know what Johnnie bought these for,' puffed Perry, fixing them to Dobbin's hoofs. 'But I'm sure he won't mind if we borrow them.'

Dobbin trotted proudly across the floor in his new shoes. Clip-clop! Clip-clop!

'When I drop the arm of the signal, start running,' shouted Perry. 'One! Two! Three! Off you go!'

The metal arm clanged down and a very strange thing happened. Dobbin felt his new horseshoes lifting him right off the ground! He whirled past Timothy Tiger and landed right at the winning-post. Clang!

'These must be *magic* horseshoes!' said Dobbin to himself.

'Dobbin has won!' shouted all the toys.

When Johnnie and Jane came into the playroom next morning, they found Dobbin sound asleep, still stuck fast to the winning-post.

Johnnie started to laugh.

'No wonder he's stuck!' he chuckled. 'Those are not horseshoes. They are my new *magnets*. They stick to anything made of metal!'

And he took them off and carefully placed Dobbin back on his wheels. But the toys were still fast asleep, so none of them ever knew how Dobbin won the race.

The Sleepy Prince

Gaylord was a handsome young Prince. But the trouble was that he was always sleepy. And this caused the King and Queen a lot of worry.

'Just look at him – sleeping again!' exclaimed the King. He looked across the palace gardens to where the young Prince sat slumped on a seat – asleep!

'Oh dear,' sighed the Queen, sadly shaking her head, then glancing up at the big clock in the palace tower. 'The dear Princess Pearl will be arriving soon. I fear she will be offended if our son should fall asleep in her company.'

'Let us hope that all the gaiety of the Fancy Dress Ball tonight will keep him awake,' said the King.

But unfortunately it didn't. Prince Gaylord actually dropped off to sleep just after asking the pretty Princess if he could have the next dance with her. Oh, she *was* cross!

Next morning, while the King and Queen were coaxing Princess Pearl to stay at the palace for a few days longer, the Prince went for a ride on his favourite horse.

Nearing the river, he was startled by the *crash!* of breaking wood, followed by a cry of 'Help!'

The frail wooden bridge across the river had broken and someone had fallen in.

Leaping from his horse, Prince Gaylord took a running dive into the river. Moments later he carried an old woman up the bank and lay her gently on the grass.

Then can you guess what the Prince did? He fell *fast asleep!*

The wet and bedraggled old woman sat up, and smiled.

It was old Wanda, the witch. In her apron pocket she carried some tiny blue berries, and when she pressed one of these between the Prince's lips he woke with a start.

'My!' he exclaimed, smiling happily as he sprang to his feet. 'Never have I felt so wide-awake!'

'Nay, you never have been really wide-awake,' said Wanda the witch, 'not since the day when I put the sleeping spell upon you when you were a babe. I did it to spite your father after he scorned my power of witchcraft. It was wicked of me. Please forgive me!'

Of course, the Prince did forgive her and went on his way feeling lively. Soon afterwards he found Princess Pearl and asked her to marry him. He was so bright and cheerful and full of life that the Princess said she would, and they all lived happily ever after.

The Donkey-Cart

Mr MacHaggart was a donkey. He lived in a warm stable on Mr Brown's farm. Every day Mr Brown's children came to the stable to feed him.

His best friend was the ginger cat. Ginger could see that Mr MacHaggart was sad.

'What is troubling you, Mr MacHaggart?' she asked him.

Mr MacHaggart shook his head sadly. 'I have everything a donkey could want. I have a warm stable, a big green field and good food.' A tear rolled down his donkey nose. 'And I have a good friend, but somehow it is not enough. I would so like to be useful. I want to be doing something.'

The cat snuggled down in the hay.

'Let us go to sleep and think about what can be done in the morning,' she said.

When they woke up they saw Mr Brown standing by his car in the yard.

'I can't think what is the matter,' he said. 'The car was all right last night and now it won't start. I promised to take the children to market this morning and they will be very disappointed.'

Ginger ran to the corner of the yard where there was an old cart.

'Mr MacHaggart,' she called. 'Come quickly.'

Mr MacHaggart trotted over to her. Then Ginger opened her mouth and made such a commotion that Mr Brown looked up at once and saw the donkey and cart.

He called to the children.

'How would you like to go to market in a donkey-cart?' he said.

The children squealed with delight. They all climbed in while Mr Brown hitched up Mr MacHaggart, and off they trotted to market. Mr MacHaggart was so proud and happy.

When they came home, very late, Mr Brown said he wouldn't bother to use the car again for market. 'Why,' he said, 'the donkey and cart are much more useful!'

Ginger had helped her friend, and she purred happily.

Bathtime

In goes the rubber duck,
In goes the boat,
In goes everything
That I can float.
Now the water's ready,
What else can there be?
I nearly had forgotten –
In goes me!

Chuff-Chuff's Good Deed

'Chuff-chuff! Chuff-chuff! Chuff-chuff!' went the little red engine as it made its way along the mountainside and round the rocky bends.

Ernie, the merry old driver with the ginger whiskers and the shiny peaked cap, was as proud of Chuff-chuff as a dog with two tails. He had driven Chuff-chuff for many years, and he kept the old engine's paint and brasswork gleaming.

Then came the most exciting day of all the days Ernie and Chuff-chuff had been together.

'Hi, there. Stop!' yelled a man who ran out of a signal-cabin beside the railway line.

'What's wrong, Sam?' Ernie asked.

'Everything!' panted the signalman. 'There's a big rock on the main line up at Windy Corner. It's a huge boulder that has rolled down the mountain. Now it's blocking the main line!'

Ernie gasped in dismay. He knew the boulder must be moved off the track before the morning express train came along and crashed into it!

Then all of a sudden Ernie brightened up and cried, 'I know, Chuff-chuff can move it. Don't worry, Sam.' And with a merry *pheep-pheep!* on the whistle, he sent Chuff-chuff chuffing away.

Up, up, up the mountain track they went until they reached the spot where the boulder lay across the lines.

'This is where you test your strength, Chuff-chuff,' said Ernie, hopefully. 'Now, . . . one . . . two . . . three . . . *push!*

As he spoke, Ernie pulled down the big lever in his cab. There was a *whoosh!* as the steam rushed down to the pistons and sent the little old engine rushing forward.

Then, *boooomp!* Chuff-chuff's front bumpers hit the big piece of rock, and to Ernie's joy it toppled sideways off the track!

It was still bowling down the mountainside below when the express came thundering round the corner, but by then Ernie and Chuff-chuff were safely on a side line.

'Well done, Chuff-chuff!' chuckled Ernie. 'You've bent your buffers a bit, but it was worth it. You're a hero!'

The Fox and the Rabbits

The rabbits lived in holes at the edge of the great wood. There were hundreds of them. The wood stretched for miles, and there were rabbit holes all the way.

One day a fox came to live in a den nearby. He loved rabbits – for supper! Every evening he would catch and eat one. He grew fat and sleek. But the rabbits grew thin trying to keep out of his way.

At last they decided it must stop. Three of them were sent to see the fox.

'Mr Fox,' they said, 'we are tired of this. Will you run a race with us? If you win you may stay, but if you lose you must go away.'

Now Mr Fox thought that he would be sure to win. Rabbits can run very fast over a short distance, but they are soon out of breath and can run no farther. Foxes, on the other hand, can run fast for a long way.

'All right,' said the fox. 'We will have a race. If you will pick the fastest rabbit I will race him for two miles along the edge of the wood. If your rabbit wins I will go away, but if I win I will stay here and have a rabbit every night for my supper.'

So in the evening the best runner of all the rabbits crouched at the starting-post with the fox, while crowds of other rabbits gathered round to cheer.

Away they went at lightning speed. The rabbit ran so fast for the first fifty yards that the fox had to gallop as hard as he could to keep up. He put his head down and went like a racehorse. He was working so hard that he did not notice another rabbit had shot out of a hole and was racing instead. The first rabbit had dropped back, tired out, and had disappeared down the hole.

So it went on, for two miles. Every fifty yards or so a new rabbit took over. The fox never noticed the difference. All rabbits look very alike. By the time they had arrived at the winning-post, the fox had raced seventy different rabbits. He was panting and puffing like a boiling kettle, his tongue was hanging out and his feet were dragging. But the rabbit skipped ahead, as fresh as a blackbird on a morning in May, and won the race easily.

All the rabbits cheered. They also laughed at the fox. They laughed at him so much that he was glad to slink away to some other place, where nobody knew about the race.

The Tallest Tree

The beech tree was the tallest tree in the small wood – but he was not the cleverest.

He could see the tops of all the other trees and he could see the clock on the village church.

The shorter trees would look up to the beech tree and ask, 'What is the time?' But the beech tree would hang his head in shame because he could not tell the time!

Mrs Rook lived in a ragged nest at the top of the beech tree with her three babies. Mrs Rook was very clever.

'Could you teach me to tell the time?' asked the beech tree.

'I'm far too busy,' Mrs Rook said.

Then she changed her mind.

'You have given me a good home in your branches. I can spare a few minutes,' she said in a kind voice.

So Mrs Rook taught the tree to tell the time. He learnt his lesson well and was very pleased.

The next day Mrs Rook was in a flap. One of her children had just learnt to fly. Now he was lost.

The beech tree peered all over the wood but could not see Baby Rook anywhere.

'He has been missing since nine o'clock this morning,' sighed Mrs Rook.

'But it's only nine o'clock now,' argued the beech tree.

'How time is dragging this morning,' said Mrs Rook.

She spent a long time looking for Baby Rook but still could not find him. Then she returned to her other children.

The beech tree looked again towards the church clock.

'Time is standing still!' he exclaimed. 'It is still only nine o'clock!'

Then he started to shake with laughter until all his leaves rustled.

'I know why time has stood still,' laughed the beech tree. 'Your baby has flown too far and is stuck on the little hand of the church clock.'

Mrs Rook rushed off to rescue Baby Rook.

'Thank you, Beech Tree,' she said. 'What a good thing I taught you to tell the time.'

Mary-Ellen's Picture

Mary-Ellen could not sleep. Mummy came in and switched on a little light, which chased the shadows away.

'Count sheep,' said Mummy as she went.

But Mary-Ellen didn't particularly like sheep, so she stared at her picture instead. In the glow of the light she could see the bright green fields, a path winding towards a blue hill, and right at the front a pink rabbit with a carrot.

Mary-Ellen stared hard, wondering what it could be like on the blue hill.

Suddenly a voice said, 'Come with me and I'll show you!'

Mary-Ellen jumped. There beside her was the pink rabbit. He held out his carrot.

'Would you like a bite?'

'N-no thank you,' she stammered, greatly astonished.

He took her hand.

'I will show you the blue hill,' he said.

They walked along the winding path, their feet crunching. Round the corner was a tiny house, with Mrs Mouse in front wearing her checked apron.

'You are just in time for tea!' she said.

'Thank you,' said Mary-Ellen, 'but no. We are going to the blue hill.'

'First meet my family,' said Mrs Mouse. Out came Mr Mouse, who shook hands, and three little mice with jam on their whiskers.

After chatting with them, Mary-Ellen and the pink rabbit walked on again. When they reached the blue hill, to her surprise Mary-Ellen saw smoke. Out of an opening came a yellow dragon. He looked pleased.

'You are just in time for a hot cake!' he puffed, and took them inside the cave. The dragon's fire sent sparks from the walls and lit up the entire cave.

He offered Mary-Ellen a cake, but it was so hot that she dropped it. It rolled and she ran after it, but it kept on rolling until soon she was deep in the dark cave.

She shut her eyes with fright. She was lost! Then she opened them slowly.

There in a glow was her picture with bright green fields, a blue hill and a pink rabbit with a carrot. And the rabbit seemed to be smiling.

The Echo

'Goodbyee!' shouted the children as they ran down the valley.

'Goodbyee!' whispered Echo sadly as he watched them out of sight.

Now it seemed very lonely among the hills. For a while Echo drifted around, then he had an idea. 'I will go and find the children,' he thought excitedly.

So away he hurried, and at last he heard them singing as they crossed a big field.

'Now to surprise them,' chuckled Echo, but oh dear, try as he would, Echo could not make a sound.

Poor little Echo! In the wide open places he had no voice.

Sadly he turned to go home, but by now the Sun had gone to bed, and in the darkness Echo wandered about, for without his voice he could not ask the way.

At last he found a nice cave, and slipped inside to rest. Suddenly the Wind came rushing in. 'Whee!' he whistled.

Echo took a deep breath. 'Whee!' he answered.

'Hullo!' cried the Wind.

'Hullo!' replied Echo.

'Are you lost?' asked the Wind.

'Lost!' sighed Echo.

'I will show you the way home,' offered the Wind.

'The way home,' pleaded Echo.

So together they left the cave, and the Wind carried Echo back to the hills.

The next morning, when the children came up the hillside they called 'Cooee!'

And Echo was so happy to have his voice again, he shouted very loudly *'Cooee!'*

At this the children laughed for joy. 'What a wonderful echo,' they cried.

'Wonderful Echo,' came the proud reply.

Mr Robinson Takes a Trip

Joey and Janey had a hedgehog called Mr Robinson. They made a bed for him in a cardboard box and put it in the shed.

One day, the children went out shopping with their mother. 'Look after Mr Robinson,' they told Tuppence, their dog.

No sooner had the children gone than Mr Robinson crawled out of his box, out of the shed and down the path towards the gate. Tuppence was very worried. He barked and barked, but Mr Robinson squeezed himself underneath the gate and waddled off downhill towards the High Street.

When Joey and Janey came back, Tuppence barked excitedly and ran towards the shed. 'Oh! Mr Robinson has gone!' cried Joey. Tuppence barked at the gate.

'I think he is trying to say that Mr Robinson went into the street,' frowned Janey.

They walked to the corner of the High Street, but there was no sign of the hedgehog. Then they met Constable Blewitt.

'Lost a hedgehog, have you?' asked the constable kindly. 'Well, if he's found and handed in at the police station, I'll let you know.'

At bedtime Mr Robinson was still missing. Joey and Janey were very sad. Then they saw Constable Blewitt pushing his bicycle up the path. He carried his helmet under one arm, and he was puffing because it was hot work cycling up the hill. The children opened the door.

'So you haven't found Mr Robinson?' they asked sadly. Constable Blewitt smiled.

'As a matter of fact, I have!' He held out his upturned helmet and there inside was Mr Robinson, sleeping peacefully! 'I found him taking a nap in the middle of a zebra crossing,' chuckled the policeman. 'So unless you can teach him road sense, ask your Dad to fix some wire netting across that gap under the gate.'

Joey and Janey were so pleased to see Mr Robinson again! He was still fast asleep as they lifted him out of the helmet and carried him back to his box. 'We'll see he doesn't take any more trips,' promised the children.

Tumble and the Baby Chick

Tumble, the dog who lived with Don at Dumbledor Farm, was a brown and white spaniel. Don's father had taught Tumble to fetch and carry. He would throw his hat across the lawn, and Tumble would bring it back. Or he would give Tumble a glove or a stick to carry.

'He's so gentle, he could carry an egg in his mouth without breaking it,' said Don's father.

One day Don heard a lot of shouting. He looked out of the window, and coming down the road towards the farm was a huge lorry. Its brakes had broken and the driver could not stop.

'Open the farmyard gates!' someone shouted suddenly.

That seemed a good idea, for then the lorry would have to go uphill and stop in the meadow beyond. Two men hurried to open the gates. There were no animals in the yard, and the lorry was now very near.

Suddenly a hen with a family of little yellow chicks wandered out of a shed into the middle of the farmyard.

'Go away!' shouted Don's father. Someone threw a stick to frighten the hen and, cackling loudly, she hurried back to the barn, and the little chicks followed on behind her.

All except one. It stood in the middle of the yard, cheeping loudly. Suddenly the lorry rushed through the yard gates, straight for the chick.

Don hurried out of doors. The lorry had passed through the yard and was slowing down as it climbed the hilly meadow.

Don's father was talking to some men. By his side sat Tumble, looking up at him.

Don went across to his father and said, 'I think Tumble's got something for you. He wants you to take something from him.'

'I believe you're right, Don,' said his father, pleased.

With his hands he opened Tumble's mouth, and there, sitting on Tumble's tongue, protected by his great white teeth, was the little yellow chick, quite unharmed. Tumble had snatched it from the path of the lorry and saved its life.

'I said he was a gentle dog!' said Don's father.

Don thought he was a very brave dog, too.

Look for other Dumbledor Farm stories in this book on pages 21, 93 and 138.

The Other Side of the Fence

Mr Green and Mr Bloom had lived next door to each other for years, but they were not very good neighbours. In fact they hardly ever spoke to each other at all, because each hated the other's garden.

Mr Green had the most beautiful smooth lawn of fine close-cut grass. It stretched from the edge of the path right up to the fence, and if so much as a single daisy dared to flower in it, he would rush out the same day and dig it up with a little fork.

'Weeds! Ugh!' he would grumble.

Mr Green hated flowers.

But on the other side of the fence there was quite a different sort of garden. It was absolutely full of flowers, all carefully cultivated by Mr Bloom. If he ever saw a single tuft of grass growing among them, he would rush out with a hoe and root it up immediately.

'Weeds! Hmph!' he would mutter.

Mr Bloom hated grass. He suspected it crept in from next door and he wished there wasn't so much of it there. At the same time Mr Green blamed Mr Bloom's flowers for the seedlings that sprang up in his lawn.

Then one night the fence fell down, probably because of too much banging by Mr Green's lawn-mower and too much pushing from Mr Bloom's plants.

Mr Bloom was horrified when he saw it and rushed out to see if any plants had been damaged. But the fence had fallen on to the grass, which did not please Mr Green at all.

For weeks they argued about whose fault it was and who should put up a new fence. But surprisingly, neither of them did!

Because Mr Green found it much easier to cut the edge of the lawn without a fence in the way and Mr Bloom noticed that his flowers were blossoming more than ever, now that they were no longer in shadow. And they both thought that the contrast of the beautiful flowers against the smooth green lawn looked very nice indeed.

A Visit to the Museum

They showed me stuffed birds in a cage
And velvet gowns from another age.
They showed me dolls and an old dolls'
house
But I saw a little bright-eyed mouse.

They showed me weapons made of stone.
They showed me a Brontosaurus bone,
They showed me medals from the war –
But I saw the mouse move over the floor.

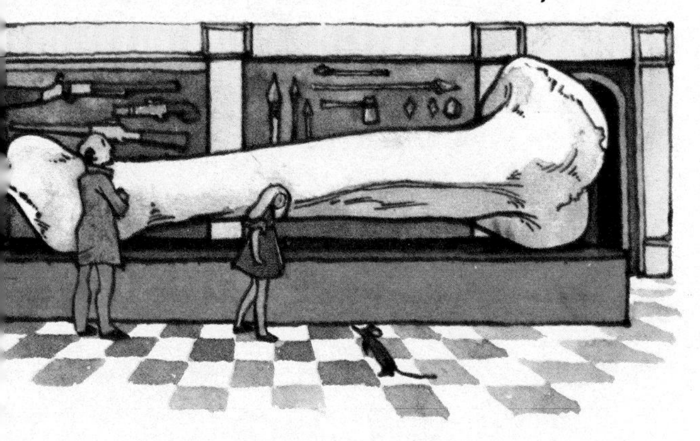

They showed me jars and old clay pots,
And coins and statues – lots and lots.
Oh dear, it's all now such a bore!
The mouse has left by a hole in the door.

Wally Mann and Mr Catt

Once upon a time there was a little boy named Wally Mann. And he went for a walk. And met a dog. And Wally Mann said to the dog, 'Good morning, Mr Dog.'

And the dog said to Wally Mann, 'My name's not Mr Dog. My name's Mr Catt.'

And Wally Mann said to the dog, 'You're a dog, aren't you?'

And the dog said to Wally Mann, 'Of course I'm a dog. I'm the finest dog around these parts.'

So Wally Mann said to the dog, 'How can your name be Mr Catt if you're a mister dog?'

And the dog said to Wally Mann, 'Well, that's what my name is.'

And then the dog said to Wally Mann, 'What's your name?'

And Wally Mann said to the dog, 'My name is Wally Mann.'

And the dog said to Wally Mann, 'You're a boy, aren't you?'

And Wally Mann said to the dog, 'Of course I'm a boy.'

So the dog said to Wally Mann, 'How can your name be Mann if you're a boy?'

And Wally Mann said to the dog, 'A boy is just a little man. When I'm a man, I'll be a big Mann; and now I'm a boy, I'm a little Mann. But when you were a little dog, you were a puppy.'

'No,' said the dog, as he trotted off. 'When I was a little dog, I was a little Catt.'

There is another Mr Catt story on page 114.

Old Slow Coach

Old Slow Coach crawled across a flat stone and sat in the middle as unhappy as could be. If only some creature would stay and talk with him. But they all seemed in such a great hurry, and Old Slow Coach was a snail.

A bee alighted on Old Slow Coach's stone, but before the snail could say 'Hello!' – off it had gone like a tiny, bright shooting star.

'I knew he would go,' sighed the snail, and he tucked in his horns and fell asleep.

A month went by and it was October.

'Hello!' said a voice.

It was a hedgehog with a spiky overcoat.

'What do you like most to eat?' asked the hedgehog. He seemed a friendly creature.

'L-l-lettuce!' stammered the snail, hurrying to answer before the hedgehog dashed off again.

But the hedgehog was still there. He was just a little tired of waiting! 'I know a garden with a lettuce patch. Come with me!'

So the snail set out after the hedgehog. He hurried as he never had before.

In November he reached the lane.

In December he fell asleep.

In January he got as far as the duckpond.

In February he ate a leaf.

By March he had crawled under the gate – but there was no trace of the hedgehog.

There were lettuces in the garden.

The snail crawled into some dead leaves and fell asleep.

In April he woke, and a voice said, 'Goodness! Who are you?'

Old Slow Coach waggled his horns. 'I'm a snail. Who are you?'

It was a long time before the voice said, 'I'm a tortoise. I've been asleep all winter, but now it's spring and I'd like a run in the sunshine. Where shall we go?'

'The lettuce patch,' said the snail.

'Then jump on my back and I will take you. Easy now – there's no need to rush about!'

The snail crawled on to the tortoise's back. He had found a true friend at last, a friend who understood him.

'You all right?' asked the tortoise, twisting his leathery neck. 'Hold tight! We'll be there a week on Monday!'

The Laughing Pony

Paddy the pony had a funny neigh, which sounded like a long laugh. He liked his laugh. But he used it in the wrong way.

He laughed at Fox limping when his foot was hurt.

'Don't laugh at me!' said Fox.

He laughed at the rabbits when their burrow was flooded and they were wet and homeless.

'Don't laugh at us!' said the rabbits.

He laughed when Mother Bird lost all her eggs and cried.

'Don't laugh at me!' she said.

And when Squirrel fell from a tree and hurt his back, he laughed again.

'Don't laugh at me!' said Squirrel.

They all became very tired of him.

One day Fox found a tin with some red paint in it. It gave him an idea. That night, when Paddy wasn't looking, he and Squirrel emptied the pony's water bucket, and tipped in the paint.

When Paddy went for a drink of water in the dark, he snorted in the bucket. That wasn't water! He shook his head crossly and snorted again to get rid of the taste.

Morning came and Paddy walked down the field. Fox was waiting. He laughed and laughed as the pony came near. Paddy stared, surprised. 'Don't laugh at me!' he said. But Fox kept on laughing.

Paddy walked away from him, feeling angry. What was he laughing at?

A rabbit popped up in front of him, took one look, and then he laughed, too.

'Don't laugh at me!' said Paddy.

He ran over to the trees. Squirrel and Mother Bird were on a branch. As Paddy came nearer, they laughed so much they almost fell off.

'Don't laugh at me!' said Paddy, really furious by now.

His owner called to him. Paddy ran over, and his owner began to laugh, too. 'Oh Paddy,' he cried, 'where *did* you get that bright red nose?'

Paddy was horrified. Bright red nose? Then he remembered his water bucket. The paint would not come off for days. Children sang, 'Paddy the Red-Nosed Pony'.

He never laughed at others again. Now, he laughs *with* them.

The Birthday Gift

It was the Princess of Catonia's birthday. The King had invited all his people to a party in the palace gardens, and everyone was expected to give a present to the Princess. It was whispered that whoever gave the Princess the prettiest gift would be given a bag of gold!

By a stream in the meadow sat a poor boy eating bread and cheese from a tin plate. Peter didn't mind being poor. He loved the life he had in the open air. He would work a few hours when he needed money for food, and then go off to make friends with the birds and animals.

Today Peter was sorry that he hadn't any money. He would have loved to give the Princess a present. He washed his plate in the stream, held it in the sun to dry, and then polished it with a piece of velvet he had found. Suddenly he laughed out loud and set off for the palace.

What beautiful presents the Princess had received! There were jewels, clothes, flowers – everything you could think of.

Into the gardens came the poor boy. He went quickly up to the Princess and with a bow he presented her with his tin plate. The King went purple but before he could scold, the boy said, 'Princess, look into the plate and you will see the prettiest thing I know.'

The Princess looked into the plate and in its polished surface she saw her own face!

'How kind you are to say I am pretty,' she said. 'Father, give this boy the gold.'

'No, thank you. I'm happy as I am,' said the boy. 'My reward is seeing your pleasure at my humble gift.' Then he bowed once more and went happily back to his meadow to sleep in the sunshine.

The Magic Carpet Flies Again

The little magic carpet now lay by the back door of the palace. He was dirty and bruised by the wiping of many feet.

When the beautiful princess was a little girl he used to fly her around the nursery. But now she had grown too heavy for the little magic carpet.

One day, an evil little wizard stepped on him and knocked loudly on the kitchen door.

'Open up, or I will turn you all into frogs,' he cried.

The plump cook hurried to the door. She bravely stood barring the wizard's way but he laughed wickedly.

'I am going to kidnap your princess and I shall not return her until the king gives me his kingdom,' he said. 'Although I am small my magic is great.'

Realising the danger that threatened his beloved princess the magic carpet shook with anger. With a great effort he rose slowly into the air with the little wizard still standing on his back.

'Help!' screamed the wizard in great fear as the magic carpet carried him away from the door of the palace. Over the rolling green lawns and over the tree-tops they flew at great speed.

'Your magic is greater than mine,' confessed the wizard. 'Please put me down and I promise never to come near the palace again.'

The carpet felt tired. As he flew over the lake he began to droop. The frightened wizard rolled off his back right into the middle of the lake. He swam away and was never seen again.

The magic carpet flew slowly back to his uncomfortable life as a door mat.

The king, queen and princess, however, and all the palace servants, stood waving and cheering from the palace windows.

The little magic carpet was then washed until all his colours glowed again, and hung in a place of honour in the throne room for all to admire.

Our Bus

We built a really lovely bus
With Mummy's kitchen chairs.
I found some cardboard for the wheels,
And boxes for the stairs.
'I'll be the driver,' Stephen laughed,
'And you collect the fares.'

My doll said she would like a ride,
And Teddy said so too.
'Please sit right at the front,' I smiled,
'Then you'll enjoy the view.'
By now, our bus is nearly full,
But here's one seat for you!

Spring Cleaning

'Help Mummy all you can,' said Daddy, waving good-bye as he went off to work. 'She is going to be very busy today spring cleaning!'

Mark and Mandy helped Mummy a lot.

They carried books out of the room and stacked them neatly in piles in the hall. They rolled up the hearth rug. They whisked up the soap-suds for the curtains to be washed. Oh, they were a busy pair and Mummy was so pleased with them!

'I don't know how I would have managed without your help,' she told them, as she covered the big furniture with dust-sheets. 'But I am afraid it is going to be very dull for you children now. I shall be hoovering the carpet and washing down the walls. You will not be able to help me with those jobs, and there is no room for you to play with your toys in here until I have finished.'

'Don't you worry, Mummy,' said Mark and Mandy cheerily, 'we'll enjoy ourselves somehow.'

They did, too. And they did not get in Mummy's way at all! What do you think those children did?

You see, Mummy had spread a large sheet over the dining table which completely covered it and hung down the sides to the floor. It made a perfect Wendy house and Mark and Mandy had a wonderful time playing inside it.

'Can we have our tea in here, Mummy?' asked Mandy.

Mummy agreed. She gave them a very special tea, too, with doughnuts and chocolate biscuits, and it all tasted so good!

'We prefer tea *under* the table instead of *on* it,' the children told their mother. 'We'd like to do this every day. We do like spring cleaning time!'

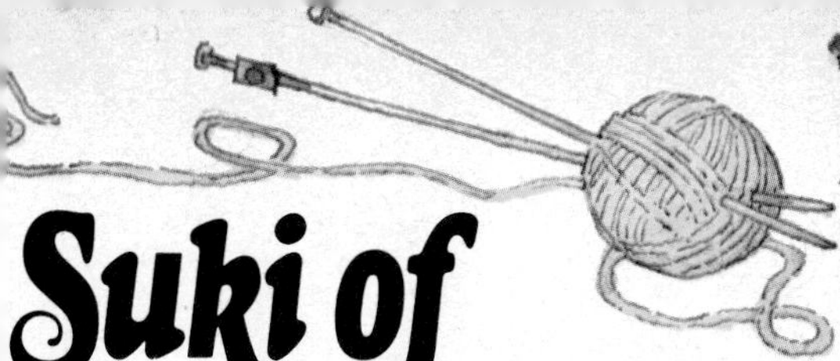

Suki of the Lorelei

Once upon a time there was a little grey kitten called Suki who lived with Caroline's Grannie in a house called the *Lorelei*.

Caroline liked staying with Grannie, but most of all she loved playing with her friend Suki. They did lots of things together, but the game Suki liked best was playing with the wool in Grannie's knitting bag.

One day Grannie said, 'Caroline! You must not let Suki play with my wool any more. Look at this terrible tangle! You know I'm trying to knit a new woolly coat for you.'

Now it was Caroline's birthday in a few days' time and Grannie thought to herself, 'As Suki is Caroline's best friend, I would like to give a little present to her from Suki.'

So she thought and thought and soon she had a wonderful idea. She wrapped up the present in pretty pink paper and wrote on the label: 'To dear Caroline from her friend Suki. Now we can have some fun playing together!'

When Caroline's birthday came and Caroline unwrapped her parcel, what do you think was inside?

A little girl's knitting basket with six balls of wool – one pink, one blue, one green, one orange, one yellow and one red, – and a little pair of white needles.

'Oh Suki! Thank you,' said Caroline. 'Now before we begin to play I think I will knit my doll a dress.'

Do you think Caroline ever made that doll's dress? I don't think she did.

Mother Candy's Golden Syrup Basin

Jonathan felt very pleased with himself. He had just made a big sponge pudding, and he was longing to gobble it all down.

'What I should really like,' Jonathan decided, 'is some delicious golden syrup on my pudding. I know just the place to get it – Mother Candy's sweet shop!'

Soon he came to the sweet shop. He peered in through the window and saw a big basin marked 'Golden Syrup'. Mother Candy was not about.

'I will pop in and help myself,' said Jonathan, naughtily.

He put the pudding down on the table and lifted up the syrup basin. But no syrup came out when he tipped it up.

Suddenly Jonathan heard Mother Candy coming back. There was no time to run away, so he grabbed the pudding and hid behind a chair as Mother Candy came in.

She was carrying a whole trayload of sponge puddings. Then, a very strange thing happened. Mother Candy picked up the basin and began to stare hard into it, chanting:

'Syrup, that I stand and gaze in,
Please come pouring from my basin.'

Out poured the golden syrup, and Mother Candy covered all the puddings on the tray.

Jonathan was amazed. It was a magic syrup basin.

When Mother Candy went out, Jonathan snatched the basin and ran home with it as fast as he could.

When he got indoors, he put his pudding on the table and held the syrup basin up. Now, what were those magic words?

Then he remembered, and cried:

'Syrup, that I stand and gaze in,
Please come pouring from my basin.'

Syrup flowed out all over the sponge pudding.

'Lovely!' cried Jonathan. 'That's enough, syrup basin. You can stop now.'

But the basin went right on pouring out syrup.

'Stop,' begged Jonathan. 'Syrup basin, stop!'

It was no use. The syrup basin began to fly all round the room, pouring as it went. Soon Jonathan's room was one big sticky, syrupy mess. Jonathan, too, was covered in syrup.

Just at that moment, the front door opened. There stood the Candytown policeman with Mother Candy, who chanted:

'Longways, sideways, bottom, top,
Syrup basin, time to stop.'

The syrup basin came quietly to rest in a pool of syrup.

P.C. Candytown looked very stern. 'Now then, Jonathan,' he said in a gruff voice, 'you have been a very naughty young man. However, I think you have been punished quite enough already. It will take you weeks to clean all this up.'

And it did take weeks! Nowadays, when Jonathan has sponge pudding, he has it with custard.

Happy Travellers

My baby sister's only small,
She sits inside her pram.
My cousin rides a bicycle –
He's bigger than I am.

My brother has a motor-bike
And Daddy has a car.
Of course, they can go very fast
And travel very far.

My Mummy journeys in a bus
On every market day.
She pays her fare and off she goes –
It takes her all the way.

The way I like to travel is
The nicest way, I've found.
I jump on my red scooter and
I scoot along the ground!

Mary Jane and the Fairy Queen

Mary Jane had first visited Fairyland with a fairy called Twink. Mary Jane had once rescued Twink when she was trapped in a snapdragon and, in return, Twink had shown her the secret way to the land of fairies.

Twink had promised that one day Mary Jane should meet the Fairy Queen. One afternoon she said to Mary Jane, 'Tomorrow when you come to Fairyland the Fairy Queen will be at home. Please bring a present for her.'

So next day Mary Jane went to Fairyland, carrying a present in a little parcel. She also took Belinda her doll. Belinda was an old doll, whose clothes were shabby and who had lost most of her hair, but Mary Jane loved her very much.

The Fairy Queen was in the palace. She sat on a sparkling throne, a silver crown upon her head and a magic wand in her hand.

'Come and sit by me,' said the Fairy Queen kindly. So Mary Jane sat on a little stool, on soft, satin cushions, and talked with the Fairy Queen. She told the Fairy Queen about Belinda and the Queen was very interested.

Then Mary Jane said, 'I have a present for you,' and she gave her the parcel.

What do you think was in it? A tooth! It was one of Mary Jane's teeth, which had come out the night before.

'Whenever one of my teeth falls out I put it under my pillow,' she told the Fairy Queen. Then the fairies come for it in the night. But as I was coming to see you I thought I would bring this one myself.'

'Oh, thank you,' said the Fairy Queen.

'The fairies usually leave five pence for me,' added Mary Jane hopefully.

The Fairy Queen laughed a lovely, tinkling laugh.

'I'm afraid I don't have five pence here, because we don't use money in Fairyland,' she said. 'But tonight one of my fairies will leave something in your bedroom in exchange for your tooth.'

And when Mary Jane woke up in the morning, what do you think she found? Belinda her doll had grown some beautiful new hair.

When Mary Jane's mother saw Belinda she said, 'I think the fairies must have spun her hair, it is so fine and silky.'

And Mary Jane smiled and said, 'I think you are right!'

There are more stories about Mary Jane in this book on pages 26 and 119.

The Missing Spell Book

Red Cloak, the wizard, had lost his spell book. Without it he could do nothing to help the queue of people waiting outside his cottage. Mrs Mophead wanted a potion to make her flowers grow. Farmer Black's hens wouldn't lay and Red Cloak had promised to cure them. Everyone needed Red Cloak's help.

When the wizard appeared the people rushed forward.

'Stop!' said Red Cloak. 'I'm sorry but I must ask you to come back later.' The people went away grumbling.

Red Cloak set off to ask Rowena the witch for help. In the wood he noticed the leaves changing colour from green to red to brown to blue and then green again.

'How strange,' thought Red Cloak.

A squirrel ran across his path. At least the back half looked like a squirrel, but on its head were two little horns! Red Cloak blinked in amazement. A pigeon perched on a nearby branch. It opened its mouth and a croaking noise came out.

'My spell book isn't lost, it's stolen!' exclaimed the wizard. 'I think I know who is playing tricks.'

He went to a tumbledown cottage where Pixie Pipkin lived. Red Cloak pushed open the door and walked in. Huddled in an armchair was a very miserable pixie.

'I'm sorry I took your book,' he sobbed. 'Nothing works properly, and look what has happened to *me*.'

He turned, showing a large bushy tail growing from the seat of his pants. Red Cloak roared with laughter.

'Serves you right!' he said. 'Where is my spell book?'

Pipkin took the book from under a cushion. 'What about my tail?' he wailed as Red Cloak turned to leave.

'Come to my cottage this afternoon,' said the wizard.

The people were waiting again outside Red Cloak's cottage. They laughed at the figure at the end of the queue. It was Pipkin, trying to hide his tail. He felt very foolish and vowed he would never try to cast spells again!

The King of the Farmyard

The animals of the farmyard argued about who should be king.

'Of course I should be king,' said the bull. 'I am the biggest and strongest animal in the whole farmyard.'

'I would be a much better king,' said the dog. 'I can run much faster than anyone else.'

'You could not find a better king than I,' said the cock. 'See how high I can fly.' And he flew up to the top of the barn and crowed as loudly as he could, *'Cock-a-doodle-doooo!'*

In the end they decided to have a race. The winner would be king. They practised for a week. The bull went thundering across the meadow. The dog raced along at his side, and the cock flew just over their heads. All the other animals came pelting along behind, but they couldn't keep up. All except the gander, and he didn't even try. He knew he couldn't win.

Then they started to argue about where they should hold the race.

'Let's ask the gander to decide,' they said. 'He can't possibly win.'

'If you promise to agree to what I say,' said the gander, 'I will mark out the course.'

They agreed, and the gander marked out the course. It went right across the pond!

The bull and the dog splashed and floundered about and got in each other's way, and the cock, trying to fly across, flopped down half-way over and got soaking wet.

But the gander swam majestically over and easily won the race. The other animals cheered. Although the gander wasn't the biggest or the fastest or the best flier, he was certainly the cleverest.

That is why the gander walks around the farmyard with a slow and stately step, holding his head erect. He knows he is the king of the farmyard.

A Very Silly Billy

Throughout the long summer, Dora the cow and her three calves, Millie, Quilley and Billy, had been left out in the fields. Now, Dora overheard the farmer planning to bring them inside.

'We're to winter in the barn,' she told them. 'There'll be fresh straw to lie on, sweet hay for us to eat, and special food-cakes.'

'Not for me,' said Billy. 'I'm not staying in all winter just for a few food-cakes!'

'There won't be enough food for us outside,' explained Dora.

'I'll find enough,' replied Billy stubbornly.

'You'll *shrink!*' said Dora. 'You'll get thinner and thinner and you'll *shrink!*'

'*Shrink!*' snorted Billy. 'Fat chance of that! I'm already bigger than Millie and Quilley.'

The day arrived when the farmer herded them across the moorland path towards the barn. Then Billy ran away!

He followed the moorland sheep and ate what they ate – which certainly was not enough for his size. And all through the winter Billy searched for more food. Finally, at lambing time, the farmer caught him.

Millie's and Quilley's eyes were as round as saucers as they saw Billy hustled into the barn.

'Aren't you skinny?' cried Millie.

'He's *shrunk!* He's really *shrunk!*' shouted Quilley.

Dora stared at Billy with large, sad eyes. 'Yes, you have shrunk,' she told him. You'll never be as large as the others again. The farmer won't waste money trying to fatten you!'

And Dora was right, for Billy was sent to market the very next day. As she watched him leave she told the others, 'There goes a very *silly* Billy.'

The Golden Bicycle

One day Pinky the elf heard that there was to be a grand spring procession through the woods.

'The Fairy Queen will be there,' he told his mother. 'Oh, please may I go?'

His mother said he could, but as the procession was to start on the other side of the wood he must ride there on his bicycle.

So off went Pinky, his old bicycle clanking and squeaking along the woodland paths.

There were many fairy folk waiting eagerly to catch a glimpse of the Queen. But when one of her guards saw Pinky's bicycle he was very cross.

'Take that rusty machine away at once,' he said. 'We don't want our Queen to see anything old and dirty like that.'

Poor Pinky was upset but he had to obey. He hid his bicycle in a clump of yellow daffodils. While he waited for the Queen to arrive, he decorated it with flowers until nothing of the rusty parts could be seen.

Suddenly the fairy folk began to shout, 'Here comes the Fairy Queen'.

Quickly Pinky left his bicycle and ran towards the crowd. Yes, there she was in a shining coach. But what was that creaking noise? Something must be wrong with the royal coach!

Sure enough, just as it was passing Pinky it stopped suddenly. It could go no further.

The door opened and out stepped the beautiful Fairy Queen.

'Can anyone help me?' she asked.

The fairy folk shook their heads sadly, unable to help. Then Pinky remembered his bicycle.

'Please, Your Majesty,' he said. 'I have my bicycle here. It is rather old, but I should be very proud if you would like to ride it.'

The Fairy Queen looked at the bicycle golden with daffodils.

'Why, it's beautiful,' she said. 'Will you push it for me?'

His face glowing with happiness, Pinky pushed his bicycle through the woods as the Fairy Queen sat sideways on the saddle. The fairy folk cheered the Queen and Pinky the elf. 'And hurrah for his golden bicycle,' they all shouted.

The Marmalade King

King Archibald was very fond of marmalade. His particular favourites were Sweet Orange and Bitter Grapefruit. He kept his castle larder stocked with big stone pots full and some of the jars were many years old.

Every morning before breakfast, King Archibald would summon the royal marmalade maker.

'Bring me a pot of last year's thick cut Bitter Grapefruit,' he would order. Or, 'This morning I'll have a vintage pot of Sweet Orange.'

The royal marmalade maker, a nervous little man, would scurry away to the larder and look along the shelves for the right pot. Then he would dip his big wooden spoon into the marmalade and taste it before taking it to the King.

One morning King Archibald awoke with such a bad headache that he could not raise his head from the pillow. The royal doctor was sent for, but his potion didn't help.

The King lay in his four-poster bed feeling miserable. Suddenly he brightened, rang his bell and the royal marmalade maker hurried anxiously into the bedchamber. Then the King said, 'Bring me some toast and Bitter Orange marmalade.'

'B – but – Your Majesty,' stammered the royal marmalade maker nervously, 'you don't like Bitter Orange marmalade. And – and – anyway, there is none in the larder.'

'Well, I like it now,' replied the King. 'I must have Bitter Orange marmalade for my breakfast so please see to it at once!'

The royal marmalade maker went back to his larder and stared miserably at the rows and rows of marmalade pots.

'Oh dear!' he sighed. 'What am I to do? There is not one pot of Bitter Orange marmalade to give to the King.'

Suddenly he had an idea. From one shelf he took a pot of Bitter Grapefruit marmalade. From another shelf he took a pot of Sweet Orange marmalade. He tipped some of each into an empty pot and mixed them together. Then he put the pot on a silver tray with a plate of toast and carried it up to the King.

'Just as Your Majesty ordered – toast and Bitter Orange for your breakfast,' said the royal marmalade maker.

'Mmmmmm, delicious!' exclaimed the King, crunching noisily. 'I feel better already. Tell me, how did you make such excellent marmalade?'

The royal marmalade maker simply smiled. 'It's a secret recipe, Your Majesty,' he said.

The Dancing Bees

Tom liked to watch the bees in the garden. They came buzzing around the flowers, and when they found one they liked they would alight on it and get busy with their long tongues. They probed into the heart of the flower and sucked out the sweet stuff called nectar which they use for making honey. When they flew away they were covered with yellow pollen dust.

There were big bumble-bees with black and orange rings on their furry fat bodies. And there were little black bees. Most of the bees, though, were brown honey-bees who lived in a hive in Mr Barker's garden down the road. Scores of them came collecting honey in Tom's garden whenever the right flowers were in bloom.

One afternoon in May the apple trees were just beginning to unfold their flowers. Tom was admiring the first pink-and-white blossoms when a bee came along. It circled and then dived in and pitched on a flower. It buzzed and fussed and buried its nose deep in the heart of the flower. Then it went humming back to the hive. Within a few minutes dozens of bees were arriving to help themselves to the newly found nectar.

Just then, Mr Barker came walking down the street, passed Tom's garden and stopped to say hello.

'I'm puzzled,' said Tom. 'How do the bees know the apple flowers are open? Did that first bee go back to the hive and tell them?'

'Come with me to the hive,' said Mr Barker, 'and I'll show you.'

A lot of bees were crawling about on the doorstep of the hive. Then one came in with some nectar. As it alighted, some of the other bees came and felt it all over.

'That bee has found a new supply,' said Mr Barker. 'They can smell and feel it.'

Then the bee with the nectar stood on the doorstep and started to dance. She flapped her wings very fast and jumped about with her tail pointing in one direction. The other bees watched her. Then, one after another, they flew off in the direction her tail was pointing.

'That's how they know,' said Mr Barker. 'The first bee directs them with her tail.'

'They are very clever little creatures,' said Tom as they walked away.

The Rock Pool

I stubbed my toe upon a rock,
I scratched my leg on limpet shells,
I tripped upon the cold wet sand,
And smelled the salty seaweed smells.

But did I care? No, not one bit,
For rocks and sky, and sand and sea
Stretched all around; and every breeze
That tossed my hair, blew just for me.

I found a pool in hollowed rocks,
A sheltered garden, warm and still,
Where water snails basked in amongst
Anemones upon each hill.

Beneath a stone I found a crab,
And two green shrimps amongst the weed,
And when I heard a shout for 'Tea',
I splashed my toes and paid no heed.

And now the holidays have gone,
The sand is shaken from my shoes,
But lying on my bedroom rug,
I sort my shells in ones and twos.

A Noisy Afternoon

Uncle Ted was trying to sleep in a deck chair under the apple tree, but his five nephews were making so much noise that sleep was impossible.

'I will give a prize to the boy who makes the best model out of sand,' he said. The sandpit was right at the other end of the garden! 'I will come along to judge at three o'clock.'

The boys ran off, and Uncle Ted pulled his hat over his eyes. At last he could go to sleep.

When he woke and saw the models the boys had made, he was very pleased. There was a castle, a lighthouse, a starfish, a car and a boat. They all looked so splendid that he could not decide which was best, so he gave them all ten pence each.

'Oh, thank you, Uncle,' they chorused. 'Can we go and spend it now?'

Uncle Ned nodded. He hoped they would buy something quiet like a jigsaw puzzle.

He had just fallen asleep again, when he was woken by a very loud noise.

'What's that?' he asked, jumping up with a start. Then he saw what it was.

The boys were marching up and down playing soldiers, and one of them had a beautiful new drum which he was banging loudly.

'Thank you, Uncle Ted,' they called. 'We put our money together and bought ourselves a drum.'

Poor Uncle Ted! The only solution was to put cotton wool in his ears.

Conky the Clown

It was just as Tina came out of the shop with Mummy that she saw something happen – the something which led to such a lovely surprise.

'Oh, look, Mummy!' Tina exclaimed. 'That old man dropped something!'

Tina pointed to an old man who had just walked past them, and then darted forward, picked a folded one-pound note off the pavement and ran to give it to the old man.

'Oh, thank you, my dear!' he said. 'I can't afford to lose that. I thought I slipped it into my hip-pocket. Must be getting careless in my old age!' he added to Mummy, with a chuckle.

He paused a moment, fumbling in the big pocket of his overcoat and drawing out two small pieces of pink paper.

'Here you are, my dear,' he smiled, giving them to Tina. 'Tickets for the circus this afternoon. I'll see you there. Good-bye!'

And away he hurried, leaving a very excited Tina with the two circus tickets.

'Oh, Mummy – can we go?' she asked.

'Why, of course, dear.' replied Mummy. 'It'll be fun.'

It was, too! Mummy laughed as much as Tina as they watched the funny antics of Conky the Clown and other exciting acts.

There was only one thing which troubled Tina. 'Mummy, the nice old man who gave me the tickets isn't here,' she said.

'Never mind, Tina,' said Mummy. 'Look, here's Conky again to do his funny last act with little Jum.'

It was a funny act, too. The baby elephant shared many of the clown's funny capers, and it was the very last one which so delighted little Tina.

Baby Jum put his trunk into a bucket of water. Then, turning to Conky, he sent a stream of water at the clown's comically-painted face – *swoosh*!

Everybody roared with laughter as Conky mopped his face. But in doing so he also washed off a lot of the paint which is a clown's disguise – and a cry of joy broke from Tina.

'Mummy – look! Conky the clown is the nice old man we met in the street! He *is* here, after all!'

A Trip to the South Seas

Annabella Jones was tired of bed. This was her sixth day of 'flu – her sixth day in bed!

She looked at the pile of books on her bed. 'I've read them all. What'll I do today?' she groaned.

'How about visiting the South Seas?' a voice asked behind her.

Annabella turned. There was a big friendly face on the bed's headboard.

'Why haven't I seen you before?' Annabella asked calmly. Nothing ever surprised Annabella.

'Everyone's too busy rushing back and forth,' the bed answered. 'Care to visit the South Seas?'

'Hmmph! How can I go anywhere when I'm ill in bed?' Annabella exclaimed.

'Hang on tight! I'll show you!' the bed answered.

Annabella grabbed her mattress with both hands. The bed rose in the air, spun around, and then sailed through the open window, much to Annabella's amazement.

Up went the bed into the sky. Annabella's home vanished beneath the clouds. The bed raced towards the western sun. Then it dropped through a hole in the clouds.

'Try this for a 'flu cure,' the bed said as they landed on a palm-tree-covered island. Blue water splashed on the shore.

Annabella jumped out of bed. The sun was warm. A soft wind blew through her hair.

'Walk in the sea,' the bed said. 'Salt water's good for you.'

Annabella waded into the warm water. Soft sand tickled her toes. Brightly-coloured fish swam between her feet. A long line of pelicans flew by overhead.

'Now, explore the beach,' the bed said. 'Let the sun toast you.'

Annabella walked along the beach. Little green turtles and pink crabs ran before her. Sea-shells lay all around.

'Time to return,' the bed said. 'That's enough sun for today.'

Annabella jumped into bed. She curled up in the blankets and fell asleep.

When she awoke her mother and father stood by the bed.

'She looks much better now,' her mother said.

'Yes,' her father agreed. 'Look at her healthy colour. You'd think she'd been to the South Seas!'

Annabella smiled and nudged the bed.

'Next time you're ill we'll go to Africa,' the bed whispered back.

Sarah Spite

Naughty, naughty
Sarah Spite
Loved to pinch
And loved to bite.

The little friends
Who came to play
Shed their tears
And ran away.

Silly Sarah!
Don't you see?
A lonely Sarah
You will be.

Naughty, naughty
Sarah Spite,
You'll lose your friends,
And serve you right!

Priscilla's Quiet Day

Priscilla Hedgehog had a lot of visitors during the winter. One very wet and windy afternoon, it was Malcolm Mole who dropped in for a chat

'I'm so glad to see you,' said Priscilla as she bustled around getting him a dish of warm milk and a slice of seed-cake. 'It's so awfully quiet here on my own.'

'Quiet? *Quiet?*' he repeated, looking at her in amazement and adding, 'Have you gone deaf?'

'Of course not,' said Priscilla crossly. 'I distinctly heard the ring-a-ding-ding of the doorbell when you arrived. Quite distinctly I tell you!'

'Then you must be able to hear all the other noises too,' replied Malcolm.

Surprised, Priscilla asked, 'What other noises?'

Malcolm put a paw to his whiskers to silence her and said, 'Ssh! Listen!'

The clock *ticked*. The fire *roared*. The logs *crackled*. The wind *whistled* and the rain *pattered*. Malcolm's boots *squeaked* as he moved his feet and Priscilla's chair *creaked*.

The tree outside the window *tapped* against the glass, and the tap in the kitchen dripped, making a *plopping* noise. Birds *chattered* over a crust of bread on the window-sill, and not only had Malcolm fallen asleep, but he was *snoring!*

Priscilla *laughed*, waking Malcolm. 'Oh my, I do see what you mean,' she said.

Malcolm stood up. 'Thank you for the tea and I have so enjoyed our quiet little chat,' he said, and his whiskers twitched with laughter.

The Little Blue Jug

There was once a little blue jug with a curly handle, and it stood on the kitchen shelf.

The little blue jug used to get terribly restless. 'Fill me! Fill me!' it cried, whenever Mum passed by.

Mum poured some milk into it to keep it quiet.

For a short while the little blue jug sat contentedly. It was full of milk and felt very comfortable. But presently it began again, 'Pour me! Pour me!'

Mum was in a fluster because starchy Auntie had come to tea. Mum had baked a cake and it hadn't risen. It was all very trying.

'Oh, do be quiet!' she said to the little blue jug. And because she was in a hurry, she grabbed it and set it on the tea tray. There it was, amongst all the best china – and what a stuck-up lot they were, those dainty cups and saucers and that fine old silver teapot!

Starchy Auntie took one look at the tray.

'Whatever is this?' she cried, picking up the little blue jug and peering at it through her gold-rimmed glasses.

'There should be a matching jug, dear!'

Mum blushed scarlet, and the little blue jug almost broke in two for shame.

And back to the kitchen it went. Mum was so cross, she emptied it and washed it, and shut it up in the dark plate-cupboard.

The little blue jug sat emptily and sobbed.

Days passed. It was really very dull in the cupboard. The little blue jug was just about to speak to an old brown teapot with a broken nose, when the door opened.

It was Mum again, with the children behind her. 'Now where's that jug got to? I'm sure I put it in here.'

The little blue jug was beside itself with excitement and rocked so violently that it fell over.

Mum picked it up.

'Oh, it's you again,' she said, dusting it with a cloth. 'Well you didn't break that time. Maybe you'd stand up to a nursery life!'

And that is how the little blue jug came to find itself on the children's supper table. It poured milk very carefully into the children's mugs, and it was never empty again for long.

The Three Princesses

Once there were three princesses who were all very beautiful. One day they received invitations from the prince of a nearby kingdom. 'Come to my ball tomorrow,' wrote the prince, 'and I will marry the princess who is wearing the loveliest bracelet on her arm.'

The eldest princess went to see her fairy godmother. 'Have no fear,' said the fairy godmother. 'I shall give you a wonderful gold bracelet all set with glowing rubies. The prince will be sure to marry you. Leave it to me, my dear.'

The second princess went off to visit her fairy godmother. 'Please help me,' she said. 'Certainly,' said the fairy godmother. 'I shall give you a beautiful silver bracelet, set with sparkling diamonds. The prince is just bound to marry you.'

The youngest princess went to see her fairy godmother, who was not so rich as the other two fairy godmothers, but who was very kind and loved the youngest princess dearly. 'Don't worry,' she said. 'I shall make you a very special bracelet.'

When it was quite dark the youngest princess's fairy godmother went out to a nearby wood. The stars twinkled in the sky. She waved her magic wand, and called to all the glow-worms in the wood to come at once to listen to her.

Next evening at the ball, the prince admired the bracelets. 'Beautiful!' he said to the eldest princess. 'Magnificent!' he told the second. He turned to the youngest and she held out her arm to show a bracelet of pretty twined leaves. On each leaf lay a little glow-worm shining brighter than any jewel.

'This is the loveliest bracelet of all,' said the prince at once. 'And you are without doubt the loveliest princess. Please will you marry me?' The princess said, 'Yes,' and they lived happily ever after.

The Runaway House

Once upon a time there was a little old house. Nobody lived in the little old house, not even a beetle or a mouse, so one day the little old house ran away.

It ran until it came to a broken-down lorry.

'Where are you going?' said the broken-down lorry.

'I am running away,' said the little old house.

'Take my wheels,' said the broken-down lorry. 'I don't want them any more, and you will be able to run away much faster.'

So the little old house took the broken-down lorry's wheels, and began to run away again.

But now that it had four wheels on, the little old house ran and ran and ran and couldn't stop running until at last *crash!* it ran smack, bang into a motor car!

'Good gracious me!' said the motor car. 'Can't you look where you're going? Can't you steer properly?'

'No, I can't,' said the little old house. 'I haven't got a steering wheel.'

'Well! Would you like me to steer you?'

'Oh yes, that would be lovely!'

So the motor car fastened the little old house on to his back bumper and off they went, rackety, rackety, bump, bump, bump, over the hills and far away.

When it was dark, they stopped in a field to sleep.

In the morning, the motor car said to the little old house, 'This is a nice little field. Shall we live in it?'

So the motor car and the little old house lived in the field, and it was very nice, with the buttercups and the daisies and the hot sunshine.

One day a pedlar man came into the field. He *was* a funny man! He had lots of pots and pans on him.

He put his head on one side, and looked at the little old house. At last he said, 'How would you like me to come and live in you? I could keep you warm and clean.'

'That's a very good idea,' said the little old house.

The pedlar man patted the bonnet of the motor car.

'How would you like me to drive you? I could keep you oiled and greased.'

'That's a very good idea too,' said the motor car.

And they all lived happily ever after.

Sally's Charm Pie

It was the day of the cookery competition and delicious smells were already filling the air. Everybody in Buttercup Hollow was busy cooking or baking – that is, everybody except Sally Squirrel.

The little squirrel could bake a mouth-watering acorn pie, but old Prickly Hedgehog, who was to judge the competition, did not like acorn pie.

Sally sadly washed up her breakfast dishes and then swept the leaves from her tiny tree room, down the winding staircase. As she opened the front door to sweep the leaves outside, she caught sight of a book lying on the ground by her doorstep.

'Whatever can this be?' she wondered, picking up the book and beginning to read.

'How lovely!' she chuckled. 'It's a cookery book and just what I need.'

In no time at all the little squirrel was busy at the kitchen table, the book open beside her.

The last part of the recipe puzzled Sally. 'That's strange,' she thought, frowning as she read on, '". . . while the pie is baking, repeat the following verse:

Sunflowers from a meadow,
Clover from a farm,
Honey from the wild bee,
Mixed together give you charm".'

Just to be sure that the pie turned out all right, Sally repeated the verse. Then with the pie in a little blue dish, and the book tucked under her arm, she set off to enter the competition.

Sally's dish was the last to be tried. By the time Prickly reached it, he was very cross indeed! He hadn't liked any of the other dishes. He tasted a spoonful of Sally's pie, then another and another until there wasn't any left. Everybody at the competition was amazed.

At that moment a wizard rushed up and, seeing the book under Sally's arm, he hurried over to her.

'Thank goodness you found my spell book, Sally,' he cried. Then he looked at the smiling Prickly.

'Good morning, Wizard,' called the hedgehog. 'You are just in time to see Sally win first prize with her really delicious recipe, charm pie.'

But Sally wasn't listening to Prickly. She was staring at the wizard. 'How dreadful, Wizard!' she groaned, putting a paw to her head. 'I have just *cooked* one of your special spells!'

'You cooked it very well indeed, Sally,' grinned the wizard, 'and it is one spell which I would not *dream* of undoing. You deserve the prize!'

Everybody agreed, and the wizard joined in the clapping as Sally collected her prize from the still smiling hedgehog. It was the thing she wanted most of all – a lovely new cookery book!

Roly-Poly

We have a greedy cousin
Who sometimes comes to stay.
We call him Roly-Poly
For he's fat and eats all day.

We took him to a party.
There was jelly and ice-cream,
And a birthday cake with icing
And candles all a-gleam.

The cake was passed to everyone –
But what a shock we got
When greedy Roly-Poly
Left the slice and took the lot!

Benjamin Bee

Benjamin was a very unhappy bumble-bee. Everyone in the whole world seemed to be afraid of him.

'Bzzzzzzz,' he used to say crossly. 'Why do you all fly away when I appear?'

But the elves were so busy jumping into buttercups and sheltering under toadstools that nobody ever answered him.

One day Benjamin visited a beautiful meadow. He knew that the sweet-smelling clover there made the very best kind of honey. Seven little elves who were having a picnic suddenly heard Benjamin zooming down out of the sky. Six of them flew away at once. The seventh, a very small elf indeed, stayed on a toadstool. Benjamin looked at him in astonishment.

'Well?' he asked. 'Aren't you going to fly away too?'

'I can't,' whispered the little elf. 'I tore my wing on a horrid thorn.'

'Dear me!' he buzzed in a very friendly voice, 'that's too bad. I thought perhaps you had stayed behind to talk to me.'

'Oh no!' said the elf quickly. 'I didn't. I was afraid you might sting me.'

'Sting you?' said Benjamin, very hurt. 'Of course I won't sting you. You must be thinking of my bad-tempered cousin, Wilfred Wasp. Now he's a nasty fellow.'

'Well,' said the elf cautiously. 'You do *look* like that old wasp. He has a furry coat with yellow stripes like you.'

'Bzzzzzzzzz,' said Benjamin indignantly, 'so that's why nobody would be friends with me! All the elves were afraid of me. Would you like me to go away too?' he said sadly.

'No,' said the little elf after a moment. 'Now you have explained, I don't want you to fly away. I'm lonely too. The other elves get tired of sitting still all day long to talk to me. I wish I could fly again like you,' he added, looking at Benjamin.

Benjamin had a splendid idea. 'I'll take you for a ride. You can stand on my back.'

The little elf gasped with delight.

'Off we go!' said Benjamin gaily. Up they went, round and round the meadow, skimming in and out of the clover patches and zooming past the buttercups.

He had found a good friend at last!

The other elves were delighted to welcome Benjamin, especially when he flew away for a while and brought back some real clover honey for their picnic.

The Little Red Lorry

The little red lorry was very happy. He worked hard taking bricks from the factory to the builders' merchants.

Fred, his driver, looked after him, keeping his engine clean and his headlamps bright.

Every morning Fred would come into the yard and say, 'Come on my beauty,' and he would climb up into the cab, start the engine and off they would go to be loaded up.

The bricks were piled into the little red lorry's truck, and off they drove to their customers. Down the narrow country lanes they went with Fred singing at the top of his voice. When they reached the builders' yard, Fred backed the little red lorry neatly round, tipped up his truck and out tumbled all the bricks.

'Well done, Fred! On time again, I see,' said the manager of the yard.

'You should thank my lorry,' smiled Fred. 'He never lets me down.' The little red lorry felt so proud he gave a toot on his horn.

When they arrived back at the brick factory Mr Adams was waiting for them. He was the boss, and very important.

'I have a nice surprise for you, Fred. I am having a new articulated lorry delivered tomorrow so you will not have to drive the little red lorry any more. The new lorry will carry many more bricks.'

The little red lorry could not believe his ears. Fred was upset, too. He liked his little red lorry and did not want a new one.

The next morning Fred and the little red lorry waited for the new arrival. Lunch time came and they waited. They were still waiting at tea-time.

Then Mr Adams came out of his office with a red face. 'The new articulated lorry is too big to get round these little lanes, and it has got stuck. So you will have to carry on driving the red lorry after all, Fred.'

Fred was so pleased he jumped for joy, and the little red lorry gave a toot on his horn.

The Magic Pear

Farmer Brown was walking around the apple tree which grew beside his back door. He was shaking his head and he looked very puzzled.

'I cannot understand it,' he said. 'I have never seen a pear growing on an apple tree before.'

Farmer Brown knew, as you do, that pears grow on pear trees.

After dinner, when he went to have another look at it, the pear was lying on the grass. He bent to pick it up, but before he could touch it, it began to bounce just like a ball. It bounced and bounced till it shot up so high it disappeared over the roof of the farmhouse.

'Goodness me!' gasped Farmer Brown. 'It must be a magic pear.'

The next morning he found a letter pinned to the tree.

It said, 'Thank you for letting our pear grow on your tree. It had to be grown on an apple tree because we needed it to feed our baby princess. Any ordinary pear would not have been sweet enough for her. Signed "King of the Fairies".'

Farmer Brown felt very proud that his tree had been chosen to grow such an important fruit.

'Thank you,' he called softly, hoping one of the fairies was close enough to hear.

So, if you ever see a pear growing on an apple tree, leave it where it is. For that one may be there for a very special reason, too.

Sleepy Jane

Sleepy Jane
Watched the rain
Pit-a-pat on the window pane.

Out in the garden she saw a frog,
Hippity-hop, hippity-hop,
Down the rockery,
Through the shrubbery,
Plop!
In the pea-green pond.

'Bed-time!' cried Mummy.
'Jane, come and wash.'
And Jane went hopping,
Skipping, jumping,
Round the chairs and up the stairs and
Splosh!
In her nice, warm bath.

The Lost Baby Hedgehog

Mrs Hedgehog looked around the floor of the shop anxiously. 'Have you dropped something?' inquired Mr Bunny, the shopkeeper.

'No, but I cannot find my baby,' she replied. 'He was standing here just a moment ago.'

'Yes, that's right, I saw the little fellow holding on to your skirt while I was serving you. We will soon find him – he cannot be far away.'

Mrs Field-mouse had just walked into the shop, and hearing this she, too, began to look. They searched under the counter, behind the piles of groceries, and lifted up the stacks of empty boxes.

'Dear me,' said Mr Bunny when they had looked in every possible place. 'Your baby is certainly not here now. He must have strayed out of the door when we were not looking.'

Wringing her hands with worry, Mrs Hedgehog ran out of the shop into the wood.

'Wait for me,' called Mrs Field-mouse. 'I will help you look for him.'

'And so will I,' said Mr Bunny, following them outside and locking up his shop.

They searched up and down the paths around the shop, but could find no trace of the baby at all.

They began looking under every bush and behind every tree in the wood, but after a time it began to seem that Mrs Hedgehog's baby really had disappeared completely.

Then to everyone's amazement Baby Hedgehog's tiny prickly head suddenly appeared over the edge of Mrs Hedgehog's shopping basket!

'Here I am, Mummy,' he said, in a sleepy, squeaky voice.

'Why, he must have climbed in there among your shopping and fallen asleep!' cried Mr Bunny. 'No wonder we could not find him.'

A Birthday Present

One morning a farmer stopped at the edge of his cabbage field and said to the farm workers, 'I want all the cabbages cut, except that row there.'

He pointed to the row growing right down the middle of the field. 'Those must be left exactly as they are.'

The rest of the cabbages were cut, put into sacks and then taken away to be sold.

A rabbit popped his head out of his burrow and stared.

'Wife!' he called, his nose twitching excitedly. 'Fetch the children, the cousins, the aunts and uncles, and the grandmothers and grandfathers. The farmer has left enough cabbages for a feast.'

Suddenly, hundreds of rabbits appeared from all parts of the field.

The rabbits chewed and nibbled away all the afternoon, and when they had finished there was nothing left in the field but cabbage stalks.

As the last rabbit crept contentedly into his burrow, two people appeared from behind a bush where they had been hiding and watching. It was the farmer and his little granddaughter.

'Thank you, Grandpa,' said the little girl, 'for leaving the cabbages so that I could see the rabbits having a feast. It's been the best birthday present I've ever had.'

My Two Dolls

Floppity Flo, my old rag dolly,
Looks dreadfully plain beside Pretty Polly!
Flo's woolly hair is black as soot,
Her body is floppy from head to foot.
Two small buttons are her eyes,
And she always has such a look of surprise!
Polly's lashes are long and her eyes bright blue.
'Good-bye' she can say, and 'How do you do?'
Her hair is fair and very curly;
Her cheeks are rosy, her teeth are pearly.
But I'll whisper a secret! You mustn't tell Polly.
Floppity Flo is my favourite dolly!
She's soft and cuddly to take up to bed
When Mummy calls, 'Come along, sleepy-head!'
Pretty Polly is very smart, I know –
But I just don't love her like Floppity Flo!

The Gnome Who Stole Stones

Norris Gnome was not very honest. He knew he shouldn't have taken those pretty stones he found down by the river, but they were just what he wanted to decorate his front door step.

'Whoever left them there obviously didn't really want them,' he said to himself. 'I had better take special care of them.'

So for the next few days he kept them carefully covered up with dry moss. Once a day he uncovered them to make sure they were still there and to admire them in the sunshine. They were certainly very attractive, with delicate speckled colouring and an unusual smooth shape.

'I really must show them off to some of my friends,' he decided. 'I will give a party.'

So he sent out invitations round to all the neighbours, and on the day of the party Norris spent the whole morning making cakes. Then just as he saw the first guests approaching his front gate, he popped outside to uncover his beautiful stones.

But to his horror he saw that his stones were smashed to smithereens! Whatever had happened?

All the visitors gathered round to see what he was staring at. Norris was so dismayed he didn't say a word.

Then someone spoke up from the back of the crowd.

'So sorry I'm late, but I've just found my dear little ducklings. Some horrid person stole my eggs, but luckily they must have all hatched and found their way back to the river.' It was Dilys Duck speaking, standing proudly at the head of a line of fluffy little youngsters.

'What are you all looking at?' she asked. When she saw Norris's stones she let out an angry squawk.

'Norris Gnome! So you took my eggs!' she cackled angrily. 'But however did you manage to hatch them? You're too small.'

Everyone laughed at the idea of Norris sitting on a batch of eggs, and Dilys Duck laughed too.

So Norris was forgiven and they all went inside for tea. And he never stole anybody's eggs again. Or anything else for that matter!

Norris had learnt his lesson well.

A Spot of Trouble

Dasher was a fine dog, and his best friend, Sam the Sheepdog, said he must enter the dog show, for he was certain to win a prize.

However, as Dasher loped across the park towards the tent where the show was being held he met Skipper, a brown dog with a black patch over one eye.

'Hello, where are you going?' asked Skipper.

'To the dog show,' barked Dasher.

Skipper looked very worried. 'Oh dear,' he grunted. 'Do you think you should?'

'Why not?' asked Dasher.

'Because you've got measles,' said Skipper, 'and all the other dogs might catch it too.'

'Measles?' Dasher was surprised. He felt quite well.

Skipper led Dasher across to the paddling pool. 'Look at yourself in the water,' he barked. 'You are covered in spots.'

The pool was like a mirror. Dasher could see his reflection. He had never seen himself before, and he stared at the water.

Goodness! He was covered in spots. He must have measles!

'You are right, Skipper. I must keep away from the other dogs,' barked Dasher. 'Thank you for telling me.'

He hurried home and sat in his kennel, out of everyone's way.

Later his friend, Sam the Sheepdog, bounded into the garden. 'Why aren't you at the show?' he asked.

'Because I have measles. Skipper told me. And you must keep away in case you catch them too. See – I am covered in spots.'

Sam laughed and wagged his tail so hard that Dasher thought it would fall off.

'That mischievous Skipper played a trick on you,' chuckled Sam. 'Of course you have spots. You always do! You're a dalmatian, and dalmatians are *supposed* to have spots!'

'Goodness me!' gasped Dasher.

'Come on! If we run hard we can still get to the show,' barked Sam.

And Dasher was just in time to win the first prize – for the finest spotted dog in the whole show!

Feeding Time at the Zoo

Mr Jones, the zoo keeper, went to feed the animals one morning. He threw a lovely piece of meat into the lion's cage.

'I'm tired of eating meat,' growled Simba. 'I'd like some fish for a change.'

Mr Jones was very surprised. He went back to the zoo kitchen and filled a pail with fish. He gave the fish to Simba, and then went to look at the penguins.

'Have you brought our fish?' asked Percy the penguin waddling up to Mr Jones.

'I'm sorry,' said Mr Jones. 'Simba insisted on having fish today and I shall have to wait for more to arrive.'

'I wonder what hay tastes like,' said Percy. 'Do you think Ranji would let me have some?'

'I'll ask him,' said Mr Jones.

The elephant said the penguin could have his hay if he could try birdseed instead.

Mr Jones gave hay to the penguins and then went to the parrot house. Sparky the parrot said Ranji could have birdseed if he could try Simba's meat.

After all the running about Mr Jones was tired. He had just sat down when Simba roared. Then there was a loud splash from the penguin pool, Ranji trumpeted and Sparky shrieked at the top of his voice.

'I'm coming,' called Mr Jones, running to Simba's cage.

'This fish smells awful,' roared Simba. 'Take it away. I want my meat back.'

Mr Jones ran to the pool with the fish.

'The hay tickles when I try to eat,' said Percy, flapping his wings in the water.

Mr Jones took the hay to the elephant.

'This birdseed won't fill me up,' said Ranji. 'Thank goodness you've brought my hay back.'

Mr Jones went to the parrot house with the birdseed.

'How can anyone eat this tough meat?' grumbled Sparky. 'I'll eat my own food from now on.'

Mr Jones smiled. He had had a very busy morning but everyone was happy at last. He didn't think the animals would grumble about their food again for a long time.

The Sausage Loaf

Once upon a time there was a fat and kindly baker who made bread for all the town people.

He mixed flour and water, sugar and salt and yeast, until he had a lovely dough mixture.

Then the baker took out his bread tins and filled each one with dough.

One day, when the last tin was filled and ready for the oven, the baker looked around and saw that some dough was left on the table.

'I know,' said the baker, 'I will fetch my rolling-pin and I will roll that dough into a lovely long sausage loaf to eat for my lunch.'

All the bread was extra good that morning and before very long all the loaves were sold and the shop window was empty. 'Well,' thought the baker, 'I *have* been busy this morning. All my bread is sold, so now I can shut my shop and eat the sausage loaf.'

Just then a little boy came running to the door to buy bread for his mother. 'You can't come in now,' called the baker. 'My bread is all sold and my shop shut.' At that the little boy began to cry.

The baker looked at the sausage loaf all golden and crusty. Then he gave it to the little boy. At once the little boy's tears stopped, and thanking the kind baker, he ran away home. Sadly the baker turned away.

Then he caught sight of his neighbour, Mrs Bright, smiling through the window and holding up a steaming bowl.

'Here you are, good baker,' said Mrs Bright. 'I have made too much stew for lunch, so here is some for you.'

How pleased the baker felt then! He thanked his kind neighbour.

Over on the other side of the town the little boy and his mother were enjoying soup and the best sausage loaf ever made!

Lucy's Baking Day

Little Lucy helps to bake
When her Mummy makes a cake.
First the butter, yellow bright,
Beat with sugar, sparkling white.
Then the eggs are really fun!
Mix them slowly one by one.
Milk and flour stir gently in,
Put the mixture in a tin.
In the oven it will bake,
Little Lucy's yummy cake!

The Three Goblins

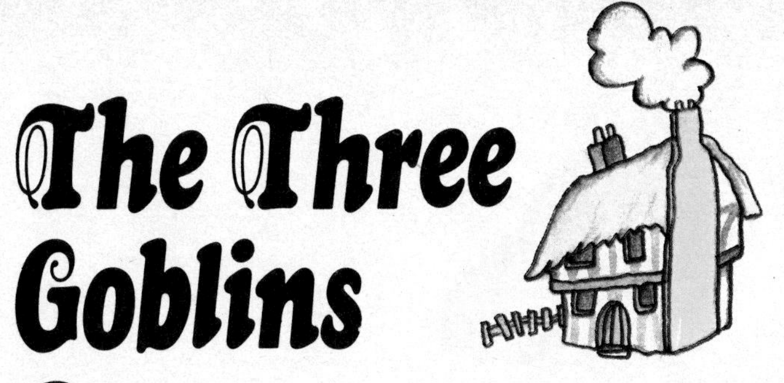

Once there were three little goblins, Hotch, Potch and Swizzock, who lived happily together in a cottage at the edge of a wood.

Swizzock was supposed to keep the cottage clean and cook the supper ready for his brothers coming home tired from work at the end of the day. But Swizzock was not so hard-working as his two brothers. He was inclined to be lazy.

One day, when Swizzock was alone in the cottage half-heartedly sweeping the kitchen floor, there was a knock at the door.

Swizzock opened the door to find a bent old woman standing on the step.

'Would you like to buy a book of spells?' she said in a croaky voice.

A book of spells! What a marvellous idea! There was sure to be a spell for sweeping floors and cooking suppers.

'Yes please,' said Swizzock, fishing in his pocket for all the money he had.

In great excitement, Swizzock sat down to read the book. There were spells for everything. He kept turning the pages until he came to a spell called *How to Make a Broom Sweep by Itself*.

Swizzock held the book in his right hand and recited: *'Grindock, grindock, hartlewhite, horny, corny, quacklepuss, badgy, wadgy, squidge, fal la la. Pop!'*

As he said '*Pop!*' there was a loud bang and a cloud of smoke. But the broom stayed where it was against the wall.

Something had gone wrong. He, Swizzock, had changed into a white cat. Oh dear. What was he to do now?

Swizzock curled up in front of the fire to wait for his brothers to come home.

At last, Hotch and Potch came home. 'Hallo, Swizzock,' they called.

'Miaow,' said Swizzock, getting up and rubbing himself against Hotch's legs. But Hotch didn't understand.

'Look Potch,' he said. 'A stray cat!'

'Out you go, puss,' said Potch, opening the door and pushing Swizzock outside.

'Where can Swizzock be?' said Hotch.

Suddenly Potch saw the spell book.

'Look, Hotch,' he said, picking it up. 'Do you think Swizzock tried a spell and it went wrong?'

'Oh dear,' said Hotch. 'Perhaps that cat is really Swizzock.' He ran and opened the door. Swizzock bounded in quickly.

'Swizzock, is it you?' Potch asked.

'Miaow, miaow,' said Swizzock, nodding his head.

Potch looked hurriedly through the book of spells.

'There is nothing here telling how to undo spells. But suppose I say this silly spell backwards. It might undo it.'

So Potch recited the spell backwards. Suddenly there was a cloud of smoke and a bang as before, and there stood Swizzock quite unharmed, and a goblin again.

'I am sorry, Hotch and Potch,' said Swizzock. 'And I promise I shall never again mind doing the housework and cooking the supper!' And he never did.

Spider's New Home

Spider the cat loved puddles. He used each one as a mirror to admire his bushy tail, his green eyes and his black fur coat. He was proud.

One day his owners moved house, but they forgot to take Spider. For a while he begged at the fishmonger's and from housewives, but he never purred 'thank you', so they stopped feeding him. Spider became a scavenger, and he looked like one. His tail drooped. His coat looked too big for him.

Autumn came. The nights were cool. Winter came. The nights were cold.

'I need a home,' said Spider to a horse he met.

'Come and see mine,' whinnied the horse.

'A field is too draughty,' exclaimed Spider.

Soon he met a mouse who invited him home. 'A hole is too small for me,' grumbled Spider.

A ladybird flew past. 'Follow me home,' she called. 'Dry leaves and cobwebs!' muttered Spider contemptuously.

A robin heard him. 'Come with me,' he chirped.

'An old kettle is too shabby,' Spider said, and suddenly he felt sad.

When he met old Miss Pink, Spider rubbed against her legs. She let him follow her home, then she showed him a tea-chest in her garden. Spider nearly said, 'It's not grand enough for me,' but managed not to.

In the night he felt a prick. Waking, he saw a hedgehog in the corner.

'This is my home!' Spider spat rudely.

'It happens to be mine,' said the hedgehog gently, 'but you may share it.'

The hedgehog gave him a prickly nudge whenever Spider sounded selfish or proud, and in time he became humble – and sleek too, for Miss Pink fed him well and loved him dearly.

Rudolf's Warning Bell

At Dumbledor Farm, where Don lived with his father and mother, there was an orchard of apple trees. Don liked to play there and to climb the trees.

One day, Don's father said, 'You had better not play in the orchard today, Don. The sheep are there, eating the grass.'

'But I *like* the sheep,' Don told him.

'I know, but old Rudolf the ram is there with them, and he is not to be trusted.'

Don knew Rudolf the ram. He was bigger than the other sheep, and he had a broad head with a black face. He looked full of mischief, and he was.

Rudolf liked to play. He did this by butting with his head. He would lower his head and charge, and if anything was in the way he hit it with a bang! Rams have very hard, thick bones in their heads, so that they do not hurt themselves when they hit something. Rudolf did not know that he hurt other creatures when he hit them. He did it for fun.

So Don stayed out of the orchard when Rudolf was there. He stood at the orchard gate and watched.

One day when Don was by the gate looking at the sheep, he suddenly saw his father crossing the orchard. He didn't see Rudolf, who was hiding behind a tree, but Rudolf saw him. He lowered his head and charged straight ahead.

'Look out, Dad!' called Don, but it was too late. Rudolf hit his father with a whack! and sent him sprawling.

'You wretched animal, Rudolf!' shouted his father, getting up and shaking his stick at the ram. 'We must do something about him, Don,' he said. Then he stormed off through the orchard towards the house.

Back in the house he found a bell and a piece of rope. Then with the help of some men he caught Rudolf and tied the bell around his neck. When Rudolf moved, the bell went 'jingle-jangle.'

'Now we shall always know where he is,' said Don's father. 'We shall be able to *hear* him, even if we can't see him!'

There are more Dumbledor Farm stories in this book on pages 21, 55 and 138.

The King's Music

'I'm bored!' shouted the King, sitting down with a thump in his best arm-chair. 'Fetch me my wise men.'

Hardly had he spoken when in rushed three men all in their long court robes, stumbling and treading on each other's toes.

'Your Majesty, how can we help you?' they asked him.

'I'm bored!' cried the King, banging his fist on the table. 'I want something new to do – what ideas have you?'

The three men muttered to each other, then the first wise old man said, 'Sire, would you like to learn to row on the river? The air will do you a lot of good.'

'Wonderful idea,' smiled His Majesty. But at the end of the day he returned looking very wet and angry. 'The boat tipped over, and I nearly lost my crown,' he stormed. 'I'm still bored! This time I'll think of an idea.'

Next morning, he heard the town band.

His Majesty rushed to the window. 'Send that band up to me,' he commanded.

They played a jolly tune and the King was very pleased.

'Would you like to play an instrument?' said the conductor.

The King was delighted. He looked for a long time at all the instruments. At last he chose a big double bass. Every day the conductor came to give him lessons at the palace, in the new music room.

One morning the conductor said, 'How well you play, Sire! Next Saturday we have a concert in Jelly Town Hall. You must play with us.' The King was thrilled.

The great day of the concert came. His Majesty was very hot and flushed when he arrived. Preparing to play, he hurriedly unbuttoned his yellow coat and threw it behind him.

The band struck up at once, and the concert went well, but the big tuba had a strange muffled sound.

After the concert, the King called for his coat, but no one could find it.

Suddenly, someone knocked over the big tuba and *plop*! – out fell the King's yellow coat! Everyone thought it was very funny and they all laughed together.

So now, whenever the King plays with the band, he is always very careful to arrive at the Town Hall early, and to hang his coat on the peg marked 'His Majesty'.

The King loves playing music so much that no one will ever hear him shout 'I'm bored!' again.

The Little Cobbler's Magic Shoes

Once upon a time there lived a very grumpy giant. He was always in a bad temper and spent his days frightening people and trampling over their houses.

Many brave knights put on their armour to fight the giant, hoping to beat him and win fame for their bravery. But the giant only laughed at them, and to make matters much worse, picked them up and threw them into the duckpond!

So the knights went to see the elves to see if they could help. 'Our magic isn't strong enough to beat the giant,' they said. Just then, a jolly little elf who was a cobbler said he thought he knew how to beat the giant. But the older elves just laughed at him and told him to go away.

That night, the little cobbler worked in his workshop making a pair of magic shoes.

The next day, the cobbler challenged the giant to a fight. The giant had never fought anyone so small. Angrily, the giant swung his club to strike the little cobbler, but to his amazement the elf leapt high into the air and tickled the giant's nose with the long feather from his hat.

When the giant tried to catch the elf, he skipped away in his magic shoes, tickling him again with his feather. The little cobbler leapt all round the giant and made him laugh so much that tears rolled down his face. Finally the giant begged the cobbler to stop, and promised never to be naughty again.

Then the giant made friends with the people and repaired their houses, so that everyone was happy. The giant felt so jolly that he asked all his new friends to a party in his own house.

Marvo the Magician

Marvo was a very clever magician. His favourite trick was taking a white rabbit out of his black top hat.

The rabbit's name was Susie. He loved her and trained her, and she was beautiful.

One day, he was showing his tricks at a children's party. The time came for the last act, and everyone was very excited. He took off his hat, showed the children it was empty, and put his hand in for Susie.

But she wasn't there! The hat really *was* empty!

He could not believe it.

He shook the hat and looked everywhere but there was no sign of the rabbit, and the children had to go home disappointed.

The days went by and still Susie was not to be found.

Without her, Marvo was very unhappy. He had an important show the next day in a children's home.

'It's no good,' he thought with a sigh, 'I shall just have to use coloured handkerchiefs instead.'

He remembered that they were in an old box, and went to find it. It was in the corner of the junk room, full of materials and things.

He put his hand in and felt for the silk handkerchiefs. Instead, he felt some fur! He pulled the materials out and looked inside.

There, looking up at him, were two big bright eyes!

'Susie!' he cried in great surprise.

Then he saw *six* more eyes!

He thought he must be dreaming, for he had found not only Susie, but three baby white rabbits, too!

Marvo was overjoyed.

'Why,' he said, 'I always knew you were a clever rabbit!' and Susie wobbled her nose in agreement.

As time went by, the little rabbits showed themselves to be every bit as clever as their mother. Soon they too appeared on the show and the children were more thrilled than ever.

Desmond's Friend

The circus marched into town with trumpets blaring and drums banging. Usually the noise brought crowds of people, but today nobody was about. The procession stopped and the music died away.

Samson, the strong man, saw a curtain flutter at a window.

'Hello,' he called. 'The circus is here. Doesn't anyone want to come?'

An old man peered out of the window.

'Go away before the dragon comes,' he hissed. 'Each day he roams the streets breathing fire. Go away quickly.'

The ring-master looked at Samson.

'You're strong enough to overcome a dragon,' he said. 'See what you can do.'

So Samson went off to search for the dragon. When night fell he returned tired and upset.

'It's only a little dragon,' he said, 'but oh, those flames! Look at my beautiful costume, it's scorched!'

Everyone sat thinking of ways to beat the dragon – all except one young man who slipped quietly away.

In his cave Desmond the dragon was crying. How could he find a friend when every time he opened his mouth flames shot out?

Footsteps sounded outside. Then Desmond saw a young man in a beautiful orange suit. The dragon tried to ask where to buy a suit like that, but all that escaped him was a sheet of flame.

The stranger opened his mouth and swallowed the flames!

Desmond sat down in astonishment. The stranger laughed.

'I'm the circus fire-eater,' he said. 'Would you like to work with me?'

Desmond is happy now. When the fire-eating act finishes each night he knows by the applause that he has lots of friends at last. And the townspeople can walk the streets in peace.

The Clockmaker's Masterpiece

Times were bad for the old clockmaker. People just weren't buying clocks.

His shop window was full of clocks. There were tall grandfather clocks that rang the hour with deep notes, and short grandmother clocks that struck the hour with high notes. There were wide clocks with fancy hands and mountain scenes painted on their faces. There were narrow clocks that told the day, month and year.

There were beautiful Swiss cuckoo clocks and French clocks that blew tiny tin whistles. There were clocks that whirled round at midday and clocks that tipped forward and backward at tea-time.

There they all stood going 'tick-tock, tick-tock'.

People stopped. They looked in the window.

'Very clever,' some said, 'but we'd like something different.' And they didn't buy.

'Very beautiful,' others said, 'but we'd like something original.' And they didn't buy either.

The old clockmaker listened. He thought for a long time. Then he went to work. For one week he drew plans. For two weeks he turned plans into metal and wood. Then he was finished.

He took the other clocks from the show window and put his new clock, his masterpiece, in their place.

People stopped. They looked in the window.

'What a plain little clock,' some laughed.

'What an ordinary little clock,' others giggled.

Suddenly they stopped laughing. They started to listen. Their eyes opened wide.

Instead of 'tick-tock, tick-tock', the clock went 'tock-tick, tock-tick'!

'Amazing! A masterpiece! How did he do it? We'll buy it!' the people shouted.

And from that day to this the old clockmaker sold every clock he made. And every clock he made, no matter how fancy or plain, went 'tock-tick, tock-tick', instead of 'tick-tock, tick-tock'.

Flying High

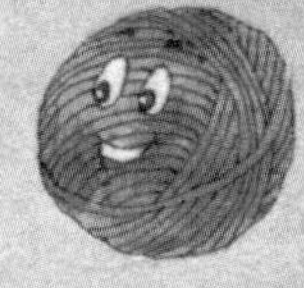

Once there was a ball of string which wanted to do something exciting.

'I don't want to be cut into pieces and tied round parcels,' it said. 'I want to do something quite different.'

It had a difficult time hiding itself away from the parcel wrappers, but it managed it. Then one day, as it lay curled in the darkest corner of the drawer, it heard someone say, 'I want some string for my kite.'

The ball of string shook itself tidy and tucked in its loose end. Its great day had come.

It winced as a length was cut from it to make a tail for the kite, but after all, that was better than having a tail made from a strange piece of string.

It was a windy day and the ball of string felt very excited as the boy tied it to the back of the finished kite. It unwound itself smoothly and evenly when the time came to unwind, and it carried the kite higher and higher into the sky.

'Who could ask for a more exciting life?' it sighed happily.

Then a gust of wind caught the kite and jerked it from the boy's hand. Up and up it flew until it caught in the church spire, and there it stayed.

'I always knew there was something special in store for me,' said the string happily. 'It's not everyone who can watch the world go by from the top of a church.'

The Good Knight's Bad Mornings

It certainly was a bad morning for the good knight!

The night before he had chased dragons till 11.30. They were burning haystacks with their fiery breath.

The night before that he had rescued captured maidens from wicked barons. He wasn't home till midnight.

And the night before that he had battled trolls in a village till daybreak.

Now it was 6.30 in the morning. He had to be on duty if anyone needed help.

But he was tired. He was grumpy. And his head ached from too little sleep.

'I'm overworked,' he groaned looking out of his castle window. 'I must do something about it.'

The knight took pen and paper and began to write letters. Then he gave them to the postman when he came with the post.

The next morning there was a knock at the castle door.

The knight opened it. Outside there was a crowd of dragons, wicked barons and trolls. 'We've your letters inviting us here,' they said in a chorus. The knight asked them into his big reception hall.

Then he spoke to the dragons. 'Do you like being chased till 11.30 at night?'

'No,' they snorted. 'We're tired after burning haystacks all day!'

'And how do you barons feel after I've rescued your captured maidens at midnight?' the knight continued.

'Very worn out,' they sighed.

'Trolls, how do you feel battling me till daybreak?' the knight asked.

'It's too much even for trolls,' they grunted.

'And it's too much for me,' the knight agreed. 'So let's make a promise to stop everything by tea-time. Dragons promise to leave hayfields then. Barons promise to let maidens go then. And trolls promise to be out of villages by then.'

Everyone's hand went up. 'We agree! Daylight for business! Night-time for sleeping!' Dragons, wicked barons and trolls cheered as they marched out of the castle.

So now you see, it's no good going to the good knight for help after tea-time.

But then, you won't have any trouble with dragons, wicked barons and trolls after tea-time anyway.

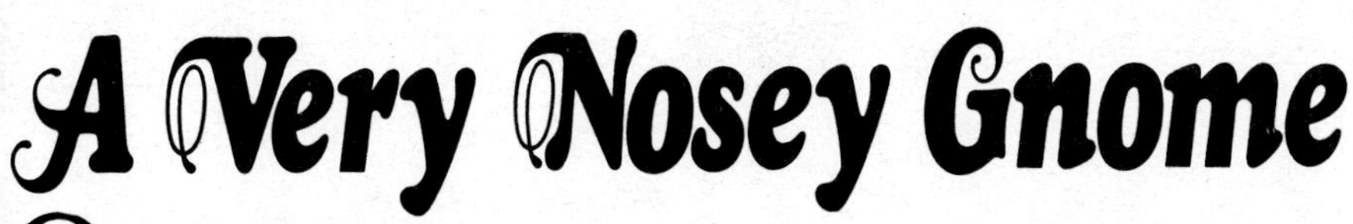

A Very Nosey Gnome

Old Dame Winkle ran out of her cottage door waving her broom. 'Go away, you naughty, nosey gnome,' she cried. 'If I catch you looking in through my window again I'll—I'll flatten your nose for you.'

Bobbin the gnome ran off down the street laughing. He had a good look to see what was in Dame Kind-and-good's shopping basket and peeped through several letter boxes.

'That gnome needs to be punished,' declared Dame Winkle to her neighbour, Dame Washtub. 'He is too nosey by far.'

All the folk in Greenville were complaining about Bobbin and his nosey ways.

When Bobbin had the cheek to go into the headmaster's private study and nose about there, Mr Slap-and-cane was furious. He called a meeting to discuss how Bobbin could be dealt with.

'Well now,' said Mr Slap-and-cane. 'I think we should fetch Wizard Cast-a-spell.'

Everyone agreed, and Pixie Speedy-foot was sent to fetch Wizard Cast-a-spell. He soon thought of a cure for Bobbin's nosiness.

'I will make a spell tonight,' he said. 'Ted the milkman can call for it before his milk-round. Pop the spell into Bobbin's bottle of milk, Ted, and I am sure you will find Bobbin a changed gnome in a day.'

Next morning Bobbin ate his breakfast and went out to see if anything was happening in Greenville. He saw Dame Grumble's box of groceries on her doorstep, and poked about in it to see what she had bought. Suddenly, his nose began to grow longer and longer and it became redder and redder.

'Oh! Oh! My nose!' screamed Bobbin. He dashed home past several Greenville folk, who laughed until the tears rolled down their cheeks.

Bobbin sat in his house and wailed, 'Oh, what shall I do? I can't go out with a nose like this.'

At last, Wizard Cast-a-spell came and rubbed some magic cream on Bobbin's nose. 'This will make it right again,' he said. 'But Bobbin, the spell is still there. If you are ever nosey again the same thing will happen and I probably won't come with my magic cream next time.'

You can be quite sure Bobbin was never nosey again.

Susan Finds a Friend

Susan lived with her mother and father at number nineteen in a big block of flats. There were no other little boys or girls living nearby and Susan was rather a lonely little girl.

'You must make your playthings your friends,' said Mummy.

So Susan did.

Every morning she dressed Teddy, her walking doll and Charlie the Chimp and sat them down to breakfast with her. Afterwards Susan would tuck them all into her doll's pram and wheel them out of doors.

'I think my friends enjoy their morning walk in the park,' Susan said. Mummy was sure they did.

But one day a dreadful thing happened. When Susan came home from her walk, Teddy was missing from the pram!

'Poor Teddy. He must have fallen out!' cried the little girl in dismay. 'We must go back and look for him. He will be so frightened!'

Alas. There was just no sign of Teddy. And it was a very sad Susan who returned home that afternoon.

Then one morning a week later, when Mummy was helping Susan tidy her toy cupboard, there came a rat-a-tat-tat at the front door. There was a kind-looking lady on the step with a little girl just about Susan's age.

'Excuse me,' said the lady, 'my little girl Sarah found this Teddy in the park last week and we have been knocking on all the doors of the flats to try to find the owner.'

'Oh, Teddy, I'm so glad you're safe,' whispered Susan, as she cuddled the furry fellow.

It really was her lucky day, because both mothers became great friends and the two little girls played together always. Susan was never lonely again.

The Peter Perkins

It was Peter's birthday and he was given lots of presents. He liked Grannie's present best of all. It was a little green boat with a tall white sail. On the side of the boat in big, bold letters was the name, the *Peter Perkins*.

'That's my name!' Peter cried excitedly to his mother, who was helping him unwrap his gifts.

The following week, when he went on holiday to the seaside with his mother and father, the little green boat went too.

Peter played with his boat at the water's edge. The tall white sail billowed out in the breeze as the little boat bobbed about on the water. Suddenly a big puff of wind caught the sail and carried the little green boat out of Peter's reach.

'Come back, little boat! Come back!' he called, but the little boat went bob, bob, bobbing over the tips of the waves and out to sea.

'Never mind,' said Mummy and Daddy. 'We'll get you another boat, just like the *Peter Perkins*.'

But Peter knew there would *never* be another boat quite like it. He lay in bed that night and listened to the waves tossing and tumbling as they chased each other up the beach.

Peter and his father were up early next morning and they went for a walk before breakfast. As they walked along the beach they stared out to sea, but there was no sign of the little green boat.

They were so busy staring out to sea that they almost tripped over something lying on the beach – it was the *Peter Perkins*! During the night the tide had come in, bringing the green boat with it.

The *Peter Perkins* never went to sea again. It goes sailing on the duckpond instead – every Saturday afternoon.

The Sailing Trip

A cat on a mat
And a rat in a hat
Decided to go for a sail.
They soon met two mice
Who said, 'Well, how nice!
We'll join you, and come in our pail.'

With very great glee
They set off to the sea,
And thought it such wonderful fun.
The mice and the cat,
As well as the rat,
All said they were glad they had come!

The Troublesome Weathercock

Once Farmer Brown had a good weathercock. It sat on the barn roof with the wind direction letters underneath, and it always pointed in the right direction. But it was old and it finally rusted away.

Then Farmer Brown bought a new weathercock and put it on the barn top. It was beautifully painted and made of non-rust metal. It would last for ever.

But there was one thing wrong with it. The new weathercock always pointed the wrong way!

If the wind blew from the south it pointed to the north. Then Farmer Brown's neighbours thought cold weather was coming. They put on their heaviest clothes and stepped outside – only to roast in the warm south wind!

If the wind came from the west the weathercock pointed to the east. Farmer Brown's neighbours thought dry weather was coming. They put on their best clothes and stepped outside – only to be drenched by sudden showers from the west. Then they had to go home and change their clothes.

One day the neighbours went to see Farmer Brown. 'Do something about that weathercock!' they spluttered angrily.

Farmer Brown wanted to please his neighbours. He sat in his kitchen all night and thought and thought.

Next morning he went outside with a ladder and screwdriver. He leaned the ladder against the barn and climbed up.

He looked at the weathercock. It was pointing south, but a cold wind was blowing from the north.

Then Farmer Brown took the screwdriver and unscrewed the letters beneath the weathercock. Then he carefully changed the letters round so that S pointed north, N pointed south, E pointed west and W pointed east.

Now – can you guess? Although the weathercock still points the wrong way, it is always right!

Benjamin Bertie

Benjamin Bertie was a little red engine who lived in a very quiet village called Little Barfold.

Twice every day he took his passengers to the junction, where they caught the big trains to the town, but the rest of the time he stood in his own little station feeling very lonely.

Ben loved the junction. The big trains often gave him a friendly toot as they rushed through.

'I wish I could go on a long journey,' he sighed. And one day to his great joy his wish came true.

It was summer time, and one morning Ben's driver said, 'Isn't it exciting, Ben! Tomorrow we are taking the village children to the seaside for a special treat.'

What a lovely surprise! Ben could hardly believe it. He was going on a long journey to a wonderful place called the seaside.

Early the next morning he was oiled and polished until he shone, and soon a merry crowd of boys and girls, with buckets and spades and little bags of sandwiches, came hurrying down the platform.

Ben was so proud and happy. He sang as he set off for the coast. But it was a long way for little Ben. He had never been so far.

'Oh dear! I hope we're nearly there,' he puffed.

'Steady, Ben,' said his driver. 'It's not far now.'

Just then they went into a tunnel, and when they came out again there was the sea rippling and sparkling in the sunshine.

There were little boats bobbing on the waves, and children playing on the sands.

Ben puffed to a standstill and the children and their teachers jumped out.

'I do feel rather tired,' he said. 'I think I'll have a little nap until it's time to go back. What a wonderful time! This is the happiest day of my whole life.'

Adventure at Night

Midge Mouse awoke late one morning. He was usually up early, long before Miss Bradshaw came down to her breakfast.

He peeped out of his cosy hiding-place in the kitchen. Then he scampered along the kitchen floor and on to the table.

'How lucky I am,' thought Midge, 'there are plenty of crumbs left for me to eat.'

Suddenly he heard and felt a deafening thud beside him. Miss Bradshaw had quietly entered the kitchen, seen Midge on the table and tried to hit him with her rolled-up newspaper. Midge scampered to his hiding-place and sat safely inside.

'I'll catch you yet, mouse!' shouted Miss Bradshaw.

All day long Midge lay in his snug hole in the kitchen wall. Miss Bradshaw seemed rather excited about something, as she kept calling, 'Fluffy, Fluffy, come along, Fluffy.'

Midge wondered who Miss Bradshaw could be calling, but he decided to wait until all was quiet.

When Miss Bradshaw was safely in bed, Midge left his hole, skipped through the wall and into the lounge.

Midge's eyes came to rest on a basket. He then had the fright of his life. Two green eyes were staring at him through the darkness.

'A cat!' shrieked Midge, and he dived for cover under a pile of newspapers.

The cat jumped out of the basket and began to look for Midge. Suddenly he pounced on the newspapers and Midge darted off. The cat leapt again, this time knocking over several plant pots which crashed to the floor with such a loud clatter that Miss Bradshaw awoke with a start and jumped out of bed.

She made straight for the lounge and tripped over the cat rushing out after the mouse.

Miss Bradshaw picked up a broom and aimed it at Midge. The cat jumped to avoid the broom and clung tightly to the long curtains which hung from the tall windows. Suddenly the curtain-rail gave way bringing down the heavy curtains, which tangled themselves around Miss Bradshaw, pulling her to the floor.

By now, Midge was back in his cosy hole in the kitchen. Fluffy looked for a means of escape. Seeing an open window, he jumped through and ran off, never to be seen again.

This pleased Miss Bradshaw a great deal. Midge heard her say, 'In all the time I've had that mouse, he's done no real damage at all. The cat I've had for one night only, and just look at the mess my house is in!' She smiled as she added, 'The mouse is welcome to stay.'

Midge curled up in his snug hiding-place and fell fast asleep.

Busy Day

Monday morning always is a very
busy time,
For then I help my Mummy hang
the washing on the line.
I carry out the bag of pegs and
hand them one by one,
And hope the wind will blow the
clothes and dry them in the sun.

The Dragon's Beautiful Umbrella

In the kingdom of Pongoland lived a handsome dragon, who could breathe flames every time he opened his mouth.

He was extremely proud of this and liked nothing better than to show off in front of the other animals. But they began to get very tired of his boasting.

One day the dragon went for a walk.

'Dear me,' he said, 'I do hope it doesn't rain. I haven't brought my umbrella.'

He looked up and saw large purple clouds tumbling about in the sky. The dragon knew that if he were caught in the rain, the water would put his flames out.

By now the first drops of rain were beginning to fall and the dragon's flames were beginning to sizzle and fizz.

Just then, a fat white goose came waddling up. She was wearing an enormous rain-hat which was nearly as large as an umbrella.

'Oh, Mother Goose,' cried the poor dragon. 'My flames are nearly out. Will you lend me your rainhat please?'

'It would serve you right if your flames did go out, dragon,' she said. 'Perhaps it would teach you a lesson.' So saying, she waddled along the path and was soon lost to sight.

The dragon sat down on a stone and began to cry.

While he was wiping his eyes he heard a cough. He looked up and saw a magnificent peacock standing in front of him.

'Oh, Mr Peacock,' sobbed the dragon. 'No one will lend me an umbrella . . . and the rain will make my flames go out . . . and no one cares!'

'Dry your tears, dragon. I think I can help you,' said the peacock.

Then the peacock raised his beautiful tail and spread it wide. It made a perfect umbrella. And such a beautiful one, too!

'There!' said the peacock. 'If you sit under my tail, you will keep dry.'

So the dragon crept under the peacock's tail until it had stopped raining.

'Thank you, Mr Peacock,' he said. 'If it hadn't been for you, I wouldn't have any flames left.'

'Well, just remember that when you start boasting about it,' laughed the peacock. The dragon laughed too.

'I'll remember,' he cried happily as he started back home.

The Lazy Caterpillar

Claude was a caterpillar. His brothers and sisters were rather worried about him because he was so lazy. While they explored the cabbage patch, Claude slept under a leaf all day.

'Good morning,' said Black Beetle, hurrying along the path. 'How are you all today?'

'Very well, thank you,' replied Chrissy caterpillar. 'But we do worry about Claude. If the earth fell in he would just cling to his leaf and sleep through it all.'

'I'll have a word with him,' promised Black Beetle.

Claude blinked sleepily when he heard Black Beetle calling, 'Come and play with your brothers and sisters.'

Not wishing to appear rude, Claude climbed down to the ground. Three cabbages further along he fell asleep again.

Then the sun clouded over. Rain began to fall, gently at first, then it poured down. The little caterpillars crept home wet and miserable.

'Where is Claude?' asked Charlie caterpillar anxiously.

Claude had been washed off his leaf by the downpour and was now struggling in a pool of water. Luckily, Black Beetle came and pulled him to safety.

Claude's narrow escape did not make him less lazy. He woke up only when he felt hungry to nibble a few leaves.

One day Black Beetle was sunning himself on a stone. A white butterfly danced down and settled beside him.

'Do you know who I am?' said the perky butterfly.

Black Beetle stared.

'I'm Claude,' said the butterfly. 'You saved my life.'

'Bless my soul!' gasped Black Beetle. 'Why aren't you asleep?'

'Asleep?' said Claude in amazement. 'I haven't time for that. Look at all those flowers I have to visit.'

Off he flitted in a dazzling dance round the flowerbed.

'How's that?' he called, perched on a lupin.

'Wonderful!' said Black Beetle. 'Nobody could call you lazy now.'

Then a tiny cloud of butterflies flew into the air. They were Claude's brothers and sisters. Claude flew round and round the flowerbed with them, the busiest of all.

The Lost Whiskers

Perkins was a handsome cat and he knew it. He sat by the fire cleaning his whiskers. Suddenly his fur stood on end! 'S-s-s-h!' he said in alarm. 'Two of my beautiful whiskers are missing.'

Mrs Muffet, the mother cat, was washing her kittens and took no notice. Perkins was upset.

'Mrs Muffet,' he said walking over and arching his back in front of her, 'something is wrong with me. Will you please count my whiskers?' He put the left side of his face in front of her. Mrs Muffet yawned.

'One, two . . . eight,' she drawled.

Perkins turned himself round, and put his right side towards her.

'One, two, three, four, five, *six*,' she said firmly.

'There you are,' said Perkins. 'There are two whiskers missing,' and he jumped on to the window ledge and went out into the night. He had decided to go and find his old friend Mr Fox.

Perkins found Mr Fox sitting in the moonlight.

'Good evening, Mr Fox,' he said politely. 'I have come to ask your help. I have lost two of my best whiskers.'

Perkins looked so sad that kind old Mr Fox decided at once to use his special cunning to help him.

'Now you lie down and have a good sleep Perkins,' he said, 'and I will prowl round and see if I can find them anywhere.'

Cunning Mr Fox waited until Perkins was snoring loudly. Then he crept up to him and pulled out two of his whiskers on the side of his face where he still had eight.

When Perkins woke up, the sun was rising over the hill and Mr Fox was sitting a few yards away.

'Did you find my whiskers?' asked Perkins anxiously.

'Well no, not exactly,' said Mr Fox. 'But I believe Mrs Muffet counted them wrongly. You go home and tell her to count them again, Perkins.'

So Perkins hurried home and told Mrs Muffet what Mr Fox had said.

'Oh dear,' said Mrs Muffet wearily. 'Now come here and turn your head on the left side. *Six*,' she said firmly.

Perkins turned round and gave her the other side of his face to count.

'Well, I declare! *Six* again,' said Mrs Muffet in astonishment.

'Hurray, hurray!' purred Perkins. 'Then I have not lost any after all!'

Mrs Bumble-Bee's New Suit

Mrs Bumble-bee badly needed a new suit. Bumble-bees are very particular about what they wear, and would never be seen in anything that was the least bit shabby.

She had been to see Mrs Needle, who did quite a bit of sewing, and she had promised to have the suit ready for her by the spring. She could hardly wait.

When the first sun shone and she saw the first flowers begin to open, Mrs Bumble-bee trembled with excitement. Off she buzzed to Mrs Needle's house.

When she brought the suit out of its wrapping, her face fell. The new suit, although very beautiful, was quite wrong. To start with it wasn't furry, and it had black spots all over it. And it was *bright red.*

'You have made the wrong suit,' she cried to Mrs Needle. 'It isn't furry, it's the wrong colour, and in any case it's much too small.'

'I don't know how that could have happened,' said Mrs Needle, shaking her head.

Poor Mrs Bumble-bee was much too upset to say any more, and she quickly flew home hoping that she wouldn't meet anyone on the way.

She hadn't been in very long when there was a knock on the door. It was a ladybird struggling with a large parcel.

'Oh, Mrs Bumble-bee,' she said. 'I didn't know until I opened the parcel that I had taken your suit instead of my own from Mrs Needle's.' She sat down to get her breath back. Mrs Bumble-bee tore open the parcel and there was her beautiful new suit. She was so pleased and thanked the ladybird.

Then she put it on and went out to join her friends in the sunshine. She *did* look handsome in it!

The Toy Soldiers

Once upon a time there was a company of toy soldiers who lived in a toy castle underneath a little boy's bed. They did not like it there very much, because it was dark and lonely.

'There was a time,' said the captain, 'when the castle stood on top of the chest of drawers, and Robert played with us every day.'

'But he was much younger then,' said the sergeant. 'He doesn't play with soldiers any more.'

'Then we must find ourselves a home with someone who does,' said the captain.

The sergeant could not see how. After all, Robert and his mother were the only people who ever looked under his bed. But the captain had a plan of action, and a few days later, when Robert's small cousin Andrew came to tea, he marched his soldiers out into the middle of the room and stood them to attention. Then they waited in a line.

'I hope the captain knows what he is doing,' said the sergeant.

Andrew was pleased when he saw the line of soldiers standing straight and brave.

'Can I play with them?' he asked. 'I haven't any soldiers of my own.'

'You can take them home if you like,' said Robert. 'I don't need them any more. There's a castle under the bed you can have, too, if you like.'

'Oh, thank you,' said Andrew. 'I will play with them every day.'

'Three cheers for the captain!' called the sergeant, as Robert helped Andrew pack all the soldiers and the castle into a box. But of course, the boys did not hear them.

Count and Play

One, the counting has begun.
Two, I'll hold a hand with you.
Three, then you can play with me!
Four, we stand upon the floor.
Five, we shake our bones alive.
Six, our legs can do the kicks.
Seven, our hands go up to heaven.
Eight, we stand up soldier-straight.
Nine, we sit down in a line.
Ten, now let's begin again!

Caroline Car

Caroline was a very tired old car. Every day her owner drove her along the busy roads. In and out of the traffic she raced, up hill and down dale. She rattled and chugged and puffed and panted as she went along.

Sometimes poor old Caroline thought, 'I just can't go on. I shall have to stop.' But she always managed.

Then one day she *did* stop. Her owner was very, very cross because he was always in a hurry. He jumped out.

'Bah!' said the man. 'You are no good any more. If you will not go, you can stay here. I'll send a tow-truck to get you and take you to the wrecker's yard. They will break you up for scrap!'

Poor Caroline. She just sagged against the kerb, too weary to move an inch further. A small tear dripped from her radiator.

But then she saw the tow-truck coming! It frightened her so much that she gave a big jump and her brake came unfastened. Before they could reach her, Caroline slid very silently round the corner and she rolled down a little hill.

She did not stop running until she was right out of the town. In the country she found a pretty little wood, and she hid amongst the trees.

'Why, what a lovely little car,' said a voice nearby.

Caroline peeped around her. Looking at her were a nice old man and woman.

'The poor thing has nobody to look after her,' said the old woman. 'Why don't we take her home with us?'

And that is exactly what they did! They only had to give Caroline a little push and she rolled right out of the wood, down a hill and up to the door of their house.

They painted and cleaned and polished her, and looked after her most kindly. And they went for gentle little drives on sunny afternoons which made everyone happy, especially Caroline!

Two Little Dogs

Once upon a time there were two little dogs and the name of the first was Teddy Tart and the name of the second was Mr Catt.

And Teddy Tart went out for a walk, and he met Mr Catt.

And Teddy Tart said, 'Hallo, Mr Catt.'

And Mr Catt said, 'Hallo, Teddy Tart.'

And Teddy Tart said, 'I'm going for a walk.'

And Mr Catt said, 'I'm going for a run.'

And Teddy Tart said, 'Shall we go for a walk together?'

And Mr Catt said, 'I'd rather go for a run.'

So Teddy Tart said, 'That would be nice.'

So first they ran a hundred metres along the road; and then they ran a hundred metres back. Then they ran a hundred metres the other way; and then they ran a hundred metres back.

Then they ran a hundred and fifty metres the first way; and then they ran a hundred metres back. Then they ran two hundred metres the first way; and then they ran three hundred metres back.

Then they sat down and put out their tongues and panted.

Then they ran a hundred metres the other way; and then they ran a hundred metres back. Then they ran fifty metres the second way; and then they ran a hundred metres back.

And then they stopped for breath.

And Teddy Tart said, 'Why, this is where we started.'

And Mr Catt said, 'Why, so it is.'

And Teddy Tart said, 'I think I shall have to go home now.'

And Mr Catt said, 'So shall I.'

And Teddy Tart said, 'Shall we have another run together another day?'

And Mr Catt said, 'Let's.'

And so they both ran home to their dinners.

Look out for the other Mr Catt story in this book on page 57.

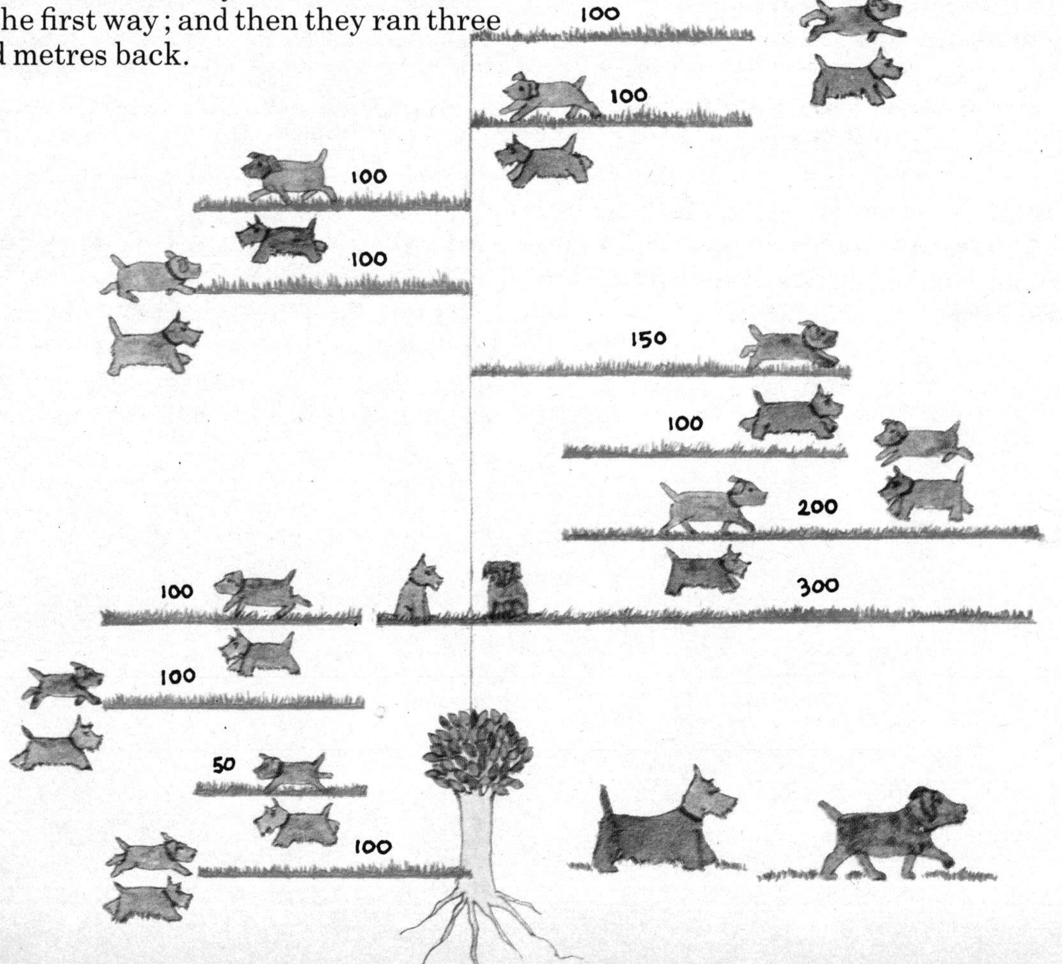

The Magic Skates

Once upon a time there was a little Dutch boy who was very poor. He was so poor that he was the only child in the town who had no skates, and so he just watched the others skating.

The richest boy in the town had a new pair of skates – the most beautiful ones anybody had seen. He was showing off when he fell over. The poor boy went to help him, but the rich boy was angry with the skates. 'It's their fault!' he shouted and threw them into a snowdrift. The poor boy was sad for he would have loved those skates.

As soon as the rich boy went away, the poor boy began to dig and soon found the skates. 'If you were mine,' he said, 'I would take care of you and keep you clean and bright.'

Although he was afraid of falling, he decided to try the skates. Then everybody was amazed – he skimmed over the ice like a graceful bird.

Soon the rich boy returned and said, 'Give me my skates!' He ran after the poor boy, who couldn't stop. The skates carried him right out of town. He was astonished, but loved them even more for saving him.

Then he thanked them and said, 'You can stop now!' But the skates led him on and on through the forests, all through the night. He was very frightened.

At last the skates stopped in an enchanted land where it was half winter and half summer, and everybody was happy. They welcomed the poor boy and asked him to stay with them for ever.

The Cuckoo and the Mouse

A mouse had crawled inside Miss Robinson's cuckoo clock and frightened the cuckoo dreadfully.

'Don't be afraid of me, little cuckoo,' said the mouse. 'I will not hurt you.'

'What are you doing inside my clock?' asked the cuckoo, its beak chattering with fright.

'The cat was chasing me,' said the mouse, 'and I couldn't think of anywhere else to hide.'

The mouse looked through a crack in the floor of the clock. 'The cat has gone,' it said. 'I will go and leave you alone.'

'That would be nice,' said the cuckoo, who was feeling rather nervous.

The mouse tried to squeeze down the way it had come, but something went wrong and he got stuck.

'Pull me out,' he squeaked.

The cuckoo pulled and the cuckoo pushed, but the mouse was stuck fast.

'Oh dear!' cried the mouse. 'I don't like being stuck any more than I like being chased by a cat.'

'Don't worry,' said the cuckoo, who was really quite clever when he stopped being scared. 'I know what to do. It's two o'clock.'

And it opened the door on the front of the clock and cuckooed – not twice, but eight times. Miss Robinson came running.

'Something is wrong with the clock!' she exclaimed. 'The cuckoo has forgotten how to count.' She took the clock down from the wall to take a look inside and there was just room for the mouse to squeeze through.

'Thank you, little cuckoo,' it squeaked as it ran to its hole.

'That's all right,' said the cuckoo. 'I needed dusting inside anyway. Cuckoo! Cuckoo! Cuckoo!'

The Little Money-Spinner

When Fairy Silk, Queen of the pretty little money-spinning spiders, saw the 'Closed' sign on Peter the shoe-mender's shop, she was most upset.

'Oh dear,' she said to herself. 'I must send one of my spinners to help him.'

So she sent along Penny, the kindest of all the little money-spinners. Unseen by Peter, Penny crept into his house and made her home in his living-room, awaiting the opportunity to help.

Her chance came one evening as Peter sat crying, for he had neither food nor fire.

Quietly Penny came out of her hiding-place and spun a golden thread from the corner of the hearth to the leg of his chair. Quickly she climbed up and settled on his sleeve.

When Peter saw her, he very gently held out his finger so Penny could walk on it.

'Pretty little money-spinner,' he said softly.

Slowly Penny walked round his finger several times, spinning him a ring of pure gold! All that evening, Penny worked her golden thread, and by daybreak Peter had enough gold to buy all he needed to carry on his work. He took down the 'Closed' sign and put up one which read 'Business as Usual'.

Once Fairy Silk saw that Peter's shop was open again, she knew it was time for Penny to leave. She told her of a poor family who had just moved into a tumbledown house at the far end of the village and needed her help.

Peter was sad when Penny told him she must leave, but he cheered up when Penny promised that she would visit him from time to time. And she did.

Our Clocks

In our house there are lots of clocks.
The biggest one of all
Is called a Grandfather because
It's very grand and tall.

The bedroom clocks all have alarms
That ring to make us wake.
My playroom has a cardboard clock
That Mummy helped me make.

My favourite is the cuckoo clock,
For every now and then
A merry cuckoo bird pops out
And then pops back again!

Miss Tilly Tidy

Miss Tilly Tidy's home was spotless. She even trained her cat, Thomas, to wipe his paws on the mat! Miss Tidy was very sensible, too – she didn't believe in fairies. 'That is all moonshine!' she snapped.

One day she was so ill she could not get up. She lay in bed worrying about the house getting dusty. 'And who will feed Thomas?' she murmured.

Miss Tidy slept for three whole days and when she woke she put on her dressing-gown and crept downstairs. Why! There was not a speck of dust on the furniture, someone had polished the silver, and Thomas was enjoying a plate of fish!

'Who has minded the house?' wondered Miss Tilly. She still felt weak, so she went back to bed and fell asleep again.

When she woke, the moon shone through the window. *Swish-swish*! What was that? Miss Tilly Tidy crept downstairs and peeped into the sitting-room. A little man in a ragged brown suit was sweeping the floor very thoroughly!

Miss Tilly remembered the fairy stories she had read as a little girl about the brownies, elves who kept people's houses tidy, but did not like to be caught doing their good deed.

Next morning she said, 'I shall sew the brownie a nice new suit as a "thank you" present!'

'Miaouw!' Thomas's fur stood up spikily. He clawed at Miss Tilly's ankle, and surely he was shaking his head?

'Ah yes!' Miss Tilly gasped. 'I remember. Brownies are upset if you give them new clothes. Now if only I could remember what brownies like. Yes – I know!'

That night, Miss Tilly put out a bowl of milk for the brownies, and shut Thomas in her bedroom. In the morning the milk was all gone. That was the kind of present brownies like!

And now Miss Tilly Tidy believes in fairies – just like the rest of us!

I Wonder

I wonder why the dandelion
Is golden like the sun;
And what makes daisy heads close tight
When the day is done.

And later when the fields are dark,
And small night creatures roam;
Do the glow-worms light their lamps
To guide the field-mice home?

Mary Jane and the Pontoguffle

Mary Jane often went to Fairyland. Whenever she wanted to go there, she just stood on a tree stump at the bottom of the garden and recited a poem a fairy had once taught her. And then she was there.

On her visits to Fairyland Mary Jane met the pontoguffles. There were usually some trotting around with the goblins and fairies. In case you have never seen a pontoguffle, it is like a large lizard, coloured blue, yellow and green, with a bright red crest along its back.

Although pontoguffles do look rather fearsome creatures, they are really quite gentle, and Mary Jane was never afraid of them. They are also very helpful, as Mary Jane was to discover.

One day Mary Jane lost a bracelet in Fairyland. It had been a birthday present from her Grannie. Mary Jane started to cry, because she knew her Grannie would be sad.

'Never mind,' said one of the fairies. 'A pontoguffle will soon find it for you.'

She called to one who was waddling along the path behind them and told him what was wanted. At once the pontoguffle trotted away, wuffling and gruffling. Before long it came back, carrying the bracelet in its mouth.

'Oh, thank you, thank you!' cried Mary Jane. 'How do you do it?'

'I can always see a blue light shining over anything that is missing,' the pontoguffle explained. 'I found this under a syllabub tree, where you dropped it.'

'Well, thank you very much,' said Mary Jane. 'I must give you something for finding it. What do pontoguffles like best?'

'Pontoguffles are very fond of mint ice-cream,' said the fairy.

So next time Mary Jane came to Fairyland she brought the pontoguffle a mint ice-cream. It was so delicious that the pontoguffle rather hoped Mary Jane might drop something else for him to find!

Look for other stories about Mary Jane in this book on pages 26 and 66.

Equal Shares

Timothy was a nice little boy, but he had one fault. He was greedy. He always wanted to be first, and he always wanted the biggest and best. He always tried to grab things before his little sister Susan could get them.

Susan didn't mind much. She was used to it. But their mother said, 'It's not good for Timothy to behave like this. He must learn not to be so greedy.'

Timothy liked eating. He liked sweets, cakes, biscuits, ices, apples and puddings. His aunt Jean, who was fond of Timothy and Susan, one day brought them a splendid cake of the kind that they liked best. It had chocolate icing nearly as thick as the cake, with hundreds-and-thousands and silver balls on top and cream in the middle.

The children's eyes sparkled when they saw it.

'Goodee!' said Timothy. 'Biggest half for me!'

'Now, now,' said his mother, 'share and share alike.'

'But I'm the biggest,' complained Timothy. 'I ought to have a bigger share.'

'Let me settle it,' said Aunt Jean.

'Here you are, Timothy,' she said, handing him a knife. 'You're the biggest, so you shall cut it in half just as you think it should be done.'

'Oh, good!' said Timothy, getting ready to cut off a small slice for Susan and keep the rest for himself.

'But when you've cut it,' continued Aunt Jean, 'Susan shall choose which half she will have.'

Poor Timothy!

He looked at the cake and then at Susan. Then he cut it as exactly in half as he could.

Rubbie Joins the Circus

Rubbie was a little doll made of rubber. It was rather soft, bendy rubber, and he was always falling over.

'He's a nuisance,' Louise told Mummy. 'Today when I was playing schools he kept flopping over his book, and when I stood him in the corner he turned head-over-heels.'

'I wanted Rubbie to be the driver for my toy train,' grumbled Mark, 'but he kept tumbling out of the engine.'

Rubbie was put away in the toy-cupboard in the playroom, and when after midnight the toys came to life, Rubbie could not help a tear trickling down his soft cheek.

'I wish I wasn't a nuisance!' he sighed.

'Cheer up!' said a gruff voice, suddenly. Rubbie saw a lion close by.

'Hello,' said the lion. 'I'm new to the playroom. I'm part of a toy circus that has just been given to Louise and Mark by their uncle.'

Rubbie was so surprised that he fell over. He expected the lion to grumble at him, but instead the lion roared with laughter.

'That was clever!' said the lion. 'I've never seen anyone go head-over-heels so quickly. Why don't you come and join the clowns in our circus?'

Rubbie followed the lion into the toy big tent. There were lots of animals there, and two jolly clowns just Rubbie's size. The toy ring-master said Rubbie could join the show that evening, and the clowns each gave him something funny to wear.

The ring-master fetched Louise's and Mark's other toys, and they all came to watch the show. How surprised they were when Rubbie roly-polyed into the ring with the clowns, and how they laughed when he turned head-over-heels-over-head-over-heels! It didn't matter how many times Rubbie tumbled over!

'I'll come to the toy circus and be a clown every night!' cheered Rubbie. 'I'm quite the happiest little rubber doll in the world!'

Only a Joke

One morning David decided he wanted to play in the garden.

'Put on rubber boots,' said Mother. 'It has been raining and the ground is muddy.'

David searched and searched for his boots but could not find them anywhere.

'I think I saw them outside,' his father told him.

'Oh dear,' said David. 'I hope they are not all wet.'

'I will fetch them while you put on your coat,' said Father, and went outside. When he came back, his smile had gone.

'Tut, tut,' he said. 'Your boots will never fit you now. The rain has shrunk them.' He held up a pair of black boots that were half the size they should have been.

'But, Daddy, boots don't shrink,' said David, amazed.

'These have,' said Father. 'I've told you before not to leave things out in the rain.'

David was feeling very sad, when a hand tugged at his coat from behind. It was his little sister, Sue, and she was wearing a pair of boots that looked much too big for her.

'I'm wearing your boots,' she laughed. 'Daddy is pretending that my boots are yours.'

'Then they haven't shrunk,' sighed David.

'Of course not!' laughed Father. 'It is April Fool's Day, and we were playing a trick on you!'

Puddles

Town puddles,
Small puddles,
Clear and undisturbed puddles,
Turning up their faces
To reflect the smoky sky.
Cold rain streaming,
Pavements gleaming,
Soon to be dirtied
By the scurrying passers-by.

Country puddles,
Muddy puddles,
Squidgy squelchy farm puddles,
Puddles that are waiting
For splishing sploshing feet.
Cart ruts brimming,
Barnyards swimming
In sticky sauce of treacle brown,
Where mud and puddles meet.

Sea puddles,
Sand puddles,
Salty hidden rock puddles,
Puddles which the waves have left
When turning with the tide.
Paddling toes bare,
Dabbling hands there,
Feeling in the slippery weed
Where shells and fishes hide.

How Wishes Come True

In the storm the big tree fell down with a crash, right across the forest path. Next morning a hippopotamus came along, on his way to the river.

'Now look at that!' he exclaimed. 'A big tree right across the path. I shall have to go round it. Oh, I do wish someone would move it away.'

And he made a track around it, through the bushes.

Next an elephant arrived.

'Now look at that!' he exclaimed. 'Fancy allowing a big tree like that to lie right across the path. I do wish someone would move it.'

And he followed the path the hippopotamus had made around the tree.

A buffalo was the next animal to come that way.

'Now look at that!' he exclaimed. 'A big tree right across the path, and nobody bothers to move it. I do wish someone would.'

Presently a party of beetles came crawling along the path. They were burying-beetles, who like to dig holes and bury things. When they saw the tree they set to work, digging a trench under it. All day long they dug, and all the next day, and for more than a week. Gradually the trench became deeper and the tree sank into it. At last every bit of the tree was below ground level. Then the beetles covered it with dirt, and no one would have known that a tree had ever been there.

Late the hippopotamus came back.

'Goodness!' he exclaimed. 'The tree has gone. My wish has come true. I can work magic.'

Then the elephant appeared.

'Goodness!' he exclaimed. 'My wish has made the tree disappear. How clever I am!'

Last of all the buffalo came and stopped at the place where the tree had been.

'Goodness!' he exclaimed. 'I never thought my wish would work! I shall have to be careful what I wish in future.'

The beetles said nothing. They were busy elsewhere, making somebody else's wish come true.

Nibbler's Wish

'I don't like being brown. I wish I were white, like those rabbits that live in Mr Bott's garden,' sighed Nibbler, who was a brown baby rabbit.

'I don't know why you keep grumbling,' said Mrs Rabbit crossly. 'You have a beautiful coat of fur. Many a rabbit would be envious of it, I'm sure.'

But Nibbler didn't think so. He just sat and sighed, and his ears dropped sadly.

'Cheer up!' cried Whiskers, his brother. 'Let's have a game of hide-and-seek.'

'All right. Shall I hide?' asked Nibbler. Away he hopped, round by the chicken-run. Now Mr Bott had left a pail of whitewash there, and Nibbler ran right into it and tipped it over. It went all over him, and he was covered in whitewash. It was all wet and horrid.

'Mummy!' he wailed, and back he hopped, dripping whitewash at every hop.

Mrs Rabbit shooed him off. 'Go away! I won't have any white rabbits here!' she cried, and she shut the door.

'Mummy! Mummy! It's me!' shouted Nibbler, rattling the door-knob.

Mrs Rabbit opened the door again. 'Good gracious me!' she said. 'I didn't know you. Into the bath with you at once.'

She filled the bath with warm water, and soon had Nibbler clean again. As she rubbed him dry, Nibbler said, 'I shall never bother about being brown again.'

'Well, thank goodness for that!' declared Mrs Rabbit.

Red, Red the Sky is Red

Red, red, the sky is red,
The sun it is a-setting.

Blue, blue, the sea is blue,
The ship it is a-sailing.

Green, green, the grass is green,
The rain it is a-wetting.

Round, round, the world it turns,
And babes we keep a-making.

The Little Roundabout Horse

The little old roundabout horse lived at the fair. Once upon a time he had been most handsome.

His red and gold paint sparkled.

His mane was soft and silky.

And when the roundabout music played, how he pranced!

The children who came to the fair said, 'We like to ride on the little old roundabout horse best of all.'

But they scratched his fine paint with their shoes.

And they pulled out his silky mane with their hands.

By and by the other animals and the fire engine (who also lived on the roundabout and were very jealous) said, 'What a shabby old horse! Why doesn't the roundabout man take him away?'

By and by even the roundabout man became ashamed of the little old horse.

'It is not worth five pence to ride on you any more,' he said.

Then he unscrewed the little old roundabout horse, propped him up in the middle of the roundabout, and screwed a smart new motor car in his place.

It was a racing motor car, which made a fine noise – grum! grummmmmm! – as the music played.

The little old roundabout horse, leaning all alone in the middle, felt quite giddy watching the racing car race round and round to the music.

Of course the children enjoyed riding in the racing car – and they liked going on the fire engine and all the other things. But they missed the little old roundabout horse. When they saw him leaning in the middle, all unhappy and giddy, they begged the roundabout man to put him back.

So the roundabout man painted the little horse, and gave him a new silken mane. Then he took the racing car away and screwed the little horse back in his place. The racing car was given a new job on another roundabout. The children were so glad to see the little horse again that they made a daisy chain and put it round his neck.

'My, you do look smart!' said the fire engine and the animals. 'Nice to have you back, little horse!'

And the little old roundabout horse pranced for joy.

The Orange Balloon

Andy won a lovely big balloon at the fair. It was orange, with a smiling face painted on it. 'It looks like the sun!' Andy said.

He skipped along the street, holding the balloon at the end of a long string. But suddenly the west wind spotted the balloon and chuckled, 'Whee! Let's have some fun!' It blew hard and up flew the balloon, tugging the string from Andy's hand.

'Hey! Come back!' Andy shouted, as the balloon drifted up towards a man who was standing on a ladder, cleaning windows.

'Please, Mr Window-cleaner! Catch my balloon,' cried Andy.

The window-cleaner grabbed at the string, but the mischievous wind whipped it away, and the balloon floated up towards the rooftop, where a man was fixing tiles.

'Please would you catch my balloon!' shouted Andy.

The man snatched at the string, but the wind gave a great puff, and up floated the balloon over the trees towards the church steeple.

Right on top of the steeple, sitting on a little platform, was a man polishing the brass weathercock.

'Hi!' yelled Andy. 'Please catch my balloon, Mr Steeplejack!'

Suddenly the west wind grew tired of its game and drifted gently away. The balloon was about to land on the sharp tip of the weathercock's tail. And then what a pop! bang! there would be. But, just in time, the steeplejack grabbed the string and pulled the balloon clear. Then he ran all the way down the steps in the church tower to the ground, just to give the balloon back to Andy.

'Thank you, Mr Steeplejack!' Andy smiled. 'I'll make sure that the wind doesn't steal my lovely balloon again!'

The Witch's New Broomstick

'Drat this old broomstick,' said Grisella, giving it a kick. 'If it hadn't been so slow last night I should not have been late for the Magic Circle meeting.' She was talking to her friend the wizard who had popped in to exchange spells.

Anxious to end her chattering, he said, 'You know, my dear, what you need is a new model broomstick, something with more power and speed.'

'What a good idea,' Grisella said. 'I'll see about it straight away.'

'I need a new broomstick,' she said to the salesman in the first shop she saw.

'A broomstick?' he replied. 'I'm afraid we gave up stocking those a long time ago. Nowadays we sell vacuum cleaners.'

'We have two models,' he told her, 'upright like this, or the cylinder type,' and he plugged them in and went whirling round the room with the machines.

'They certainly seem to have speed and power,' she thought, and she asked the salesman to deliver them to her cottage.

'I shan't need those long pieces of string,' she told him. 'You may keep those.'

'But madam,' said the salesman, 'they won't go without the electric leads.'

'Nonsense,' said Grisella as she swept out of the shop, 'just the machines, please.'

How excited Grisella was when they arrived!

First Grisella leapt on to the cylinder cleaner and was whirled out through the door and over the rooftops.

'Whee!' she shouted. 'This is exciting. But then – disaster! As she turned for home, the cleaner whipped around like a snake, and being new and slippery, went zipping off through the night without its passenger.

Grisella was not hurt, of course; witches do not wear long, full black skirts for nothing, and her skirt billowed out and carried her to earth like a parachute.

The next day, away went Grisella on her upright cleaner, and this time everything was fine.

What a sensation Grisella caused at the next Magic Circle meeting! She was the first to arrive and she was never late again.

Pip Mouse Goes Shopping

Jackie Mouse, Billy Mouse and Pip Mouse were going shopping. At least, Jackie Mouse and Billy Mouse were going shopping, and Pip Mouse, their brother, was being allowed to go with them for a treat.

'Now,' said Mother, 'I want you to go to Mr Squirrel's shop and buy some nuts. Here is a bag to carry them home in, and don't be late for lunch.'

So they put on their warm coats with the big pockets, and they put on their warm woolly hats, and off they went. Mr Squirrel's shop was at the end of the field, under the old oak tree.

Mr Squirrel filled their bag with nuts. and they began to walk home. Jackie and Billy carried the bag between them, and Pip walked behind.

They had not gone far, when all of a sudden there was a noise of tearing paper, and all the nuts fell out of the bag in a heap on the ground.

'Oh, dear!' said Jackie.

'Whatever shall we do?' said Billy.

'We shall just have to go home and fetch another bag,' said Jackie, crossly. 'And we shall be late for lunch.'

But Pip was not listening to them. He was busy picking up the nuts and putting them into his pockets.

'What a good idea!' said Jackie Mouse, and they all stuffed in as many nuts as they could, until their pockets were quite full up.

'Whatever shall we do?' said Billy. 'There are still a lot of nuts left on the ground, and we can't get another nut in our pockets.'

But Pip was not listening to him. He had taken off his woolly hat and was busy picking up the nuts and putting them into it as fast as he could.

'What a good idea!' said Jackie Mouse.

And when they had picked up all the nuts in their hats, they carried them home in time for lunch.

Mother was pleased when Jackie and Billy told her how Pip had helped them, and she gave Pip an extra big nut for his lunch.

The Jackdaw and the Milk Money

One morning, when Barney's mother came downstairs to make the breakfast, she remembered that there was no milk. She called to Barney.

'Here is a ten pence piece. Now mind you don't lose it. Run and get some milk for our breakfast.'

Barney ran off down the road as fast as he could to find the milkman. It had been raining hard and Barney wasn't really looking where he was going, and suddenly, *splish-splosh!* over he went right in the middle of a very large puddle. The ten pence piece flew out of his hand.

As he picked himself up Barney saw the jackdaw. Quick as anything it swooped down, picked up Barney's money, gave a little hop and a jump, and flew off.

'Oh dear,' thought Barney miserably, 'now what shall I do? Mummy will be so cross, and I'm dreadfully wet.'

Barney was very unhappy, and as he walked home he knew his mother would never believe that a jackdaw had stolen the money.

Well of course, she didn't. She was very angry that Barney should make up such a story, and get his clothes so wet that they had to be changed right down to his vest.

When he had put on fresh clothes and hung his wet things to dry, they sat down to eat their dry cornflakes.

Suddenly they heard a tapping on the window, and they looked up to see the jackdaw sitting on the window-sill with the ten pence piece in its beak.

'Well I never,' said Barney's mother. 'I would never have believed it.'

Barney looked at the jackdaw and laughed. Barney's mother looked at Barney and laughed.

And as the jackdaw flew away with the coin still in its beak, Barney was sure it was laughing too!

Secret Things

I have a pocket
For secret things,
Personal belongings
And stuff like that.

Nobody knows of
My secret things,
Not even Daddy
And that's a fact.

The contents within
Are precious you see,
And no one shall
Know of them –
Only me.

Fog in the Woods

When Oliver the Owl awoke, he could see nothing. Not a single thing.

'Ouuu, Ouuu,' he said in his deep voice. 'Everything's disappeared!'

Everything had not *really* disappeared, for all was hidden in a thick, thick fog.

Presently Oliver heard rustlings on the path below. Curious, he flew down to find out what was happening.

There were Badger and the Squirrel family, who lived in the same tree as Oliver, Mr and Mrs Hare and the rabbits from over the way.

'Hell*ouuu*,' said Oliver in his deep, deep voice. 'What's going on?'

'We're off to Stoat's birthday party,' said Badger. 'We're just waiting for Owen the Glow-worm to show up.'

Just then, Oliver saw Owen's emerald green light, glowing through the fog, weaving its way towards them. He stayed to watch the animals arrange themselves in single file, each holding the tail or ear of the one in front. Then Owen glowed his way down the line before taking his position at their head and leading off.

The merry little party had made Oliver restless, so he called up his friend Blinkie. First he gave two deep, deep hoots and then he called:

'Twit-twoo. Twit-twoo.
Blinkie, are you fog-bound too?'

Back came the reply in a voice even deeper:

'Thick, thick fog is here to stay.
Suggest tonight we do not stray.'

So Oliver flew back to his tree-top perch. He ruffled his feathers – just once – and then settled down to sleep.

The Squirrel and the Mouse

Twiggy the squirrel was concerned about his winter store of nuts. He knew it was his own fault because he was so lazy. Instead of working during the day he just went to sleep. He hardly had any food for the coming winter and he had to think of something quickly.

'Have you any ideas?' he asked his friend Beaver.

'Yes,' said Beaver kindly. 'Get to work, you lazy squirrel. If you work extra hard you will be able to collect a lot of nuts in a short time.'

Twiggy did not like the sound of this, but he sat down to think about it. Within minutes he was fast asleep. He slept for hours, while all his friends were busily working around him.

One day, as Twiggy was dozing at the foot of the tree, he was woken by the sound of someone crying. He looked around and saw a little mouse sobbing bitterly.

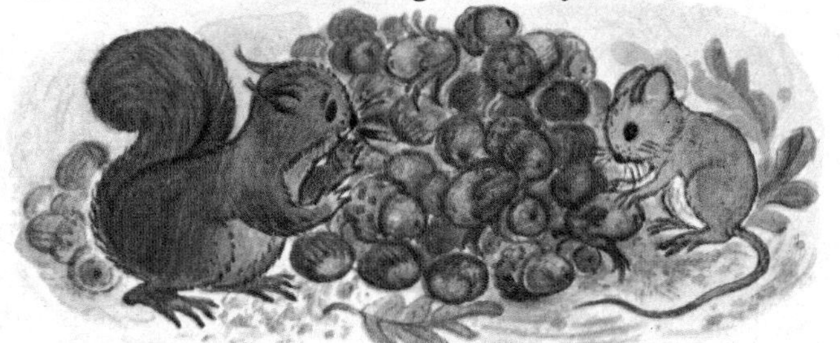

'What is the matter, Mouse?' asked Twiggy gently.

The mouse rubbed his eyes with his two front feet and sighed. 'I cannot find anywhere to sleep for the winter. I am frightened I'll freeze to death.'

'I have a problem, too,' said Twiggy. 'I have not saved any food for the winter. I'm frightened I'll starve to death.'

So they sat and tried to think of a good idea for each other.

Twiggy soon fell asleep and so the mouse curled up in the squirrel's lovely bushy tail and waited for him to wake up.

When Twiggy awoke at last, the mouse said, 'What a lovely cosy tail you have. I was as warm as toast curled up there.'

'That's it,' cried Twiggy. 'We have found you a sleeping place.'

'Have we?' said the mouse. 'Where is it then?'

'In my tail,' laughed Twiggy.

The mouse was surprised. 'Do you really mean it?'

'I will love having you to stay,' replied Twiggy. Then he promptly fell asleep again.

The mouse was pleased and wanted to repay the kind squirrel in some way.

'I know,' he said to himself. 'I will collect the nuts for the food store.' So he set to work at once and he was the busiest person in the whole forest. The next time Twiggy looked in his cellar he could hardly believe his eyes.

'A full store,' he gasped in surprise. 'How wonderful!'

So when the cold winter arrived two friends curled up happily.

The Unforgettable Present

'This time you've gone too far,' shouted Mr Pimm, 'just look at my head!' and he took off his hat. The wizard gazed at Mr Pimm's head in dismay. It was covered with a healthy crop of mushrooms!

'Oh dear,' said the wizard, 'I know somebody asked me to improve their mushrooms; I wonder who has my special hair-growing cream? If you'll sit down, Mr Pimm, I'll make a new lotion.'

'I wish I could remember my name,' he thought. 'It's rather undignified just being called "the wizard".' He finished and handed the new cream to Mr Pimm, who was quite red in the face with anger.

'It had better work this time, or we shall be needing a new wizard in the village,' Mr Pimm said, as he crammed his hat over his head and departed.

'Oh dear,' thought the wizard, 'that would be terrible.'

The wizard sighed, and was so frightened that he did not answer the postman's knock, thinking that it must be another angry customer.

'Letter for you, Wizard,' shouted the postman, pushing it under the door.

The wizard opened it eagerly and saw it was from his uncle.

'Dear Nephew,' the letter began, 'I am sending you a present as I have been hearing sad news about your forgetfulness. It should walk in on Friday. Treat it well, and remember, they never forget! Your uncle, Grand Wizard.'

The wizard *was* pleased.

'How nice to have a present when it's not my birthday,' he thought, 'but whatever can it be that is going to walk in and never forget? I wish I could remember when it's Friday.' He sat down to think hard, but he was so weary that he soon fell asleep in his armchair.

The wizard awoke as a great pounding shook the house. He clutched the arms of his chair and stared straight ahead.

'Gracious, I'm still dreaming,' he gasped as he stared at a large grey object with two huge ears and a trunk. 'Whatever is an elephant doing here?'

'It's Friday,' boomed a deep voice, 'and your name is Egbert.'

'Of course, of course,' said the wizard, 'no wonder I couldn't remember such an awful name. How did you know?'

'Your uncle told me,' replied the elephant. 'I'm his present.'

The wizard was delighted. Never again was he allowed to make silly mistakes, for the elephant never forgot anything.

A New Doll for Blossom

Billy and Blossom, the young hippos, were shopping. It was Blossom's birthday and Billy was buying her a present.

'Now, what would you like?' said Billy.

'A hippo doll,' said Blossom.

'Oh dear,' said Billy, 'I do not think they make them. But we will look.'

Billy and Blossom looked all round the shop. There were many kinds of doll, but no hippo doll.

'We will look at the soft toys,' said Billy. 'I think they might have a hippo there.'

There were bears and monkeys and rabbits. There were donkeys and horses and elephants. There were even camels, lions and giraffes. But there was no hippo.

Blossom was very disappointed.

'Does no one want to play with a toy like me?' she said sadly.

Billy did not know what to say.

Now the owner of the shop had been listening to Billy and Blossom. He smiled at Blossom.

'Tell me, madam,' he said, 'just how would you make a soft cuddly hippo like yourself?'

'Well,' said Blossom dreamily, 'I should make it in soft grey velvet, and fill it with nice squashy rubber. I should give it kind twinkling eyes and a big curly smiling mouth. I should put a nice "grunt" in its tummy. Then, when I talked to it, it would go "Mmnm—mnmn!" back.'

The shopman shook Blossom's hoof.

'Thank you very much!' he cried. 'I had quite run out of new ideas for toys. Now you have given me a splendid new one. Please come back next week. I hope I will have a surprise for you.'

The next week they came back. There in the window sat a big, grey velvet hippo, with twinkling eyes. *'New!'* said the notice above it, 'Cuddly Blossoms'.

The shopkeeper hurried out.

'Come right in,' he said. 'All the children are wanting a cuddly hippo. It was a splendid idea! Allow me to give you one of your very own.'

'Oh thank you,' said Blossom, giving her grey velvet hippo a loving hug. 'It is the best birthday present I have ever had!'

Gribble's New Hat

Gribble made her witches work very hard. When they weren't making spells in the kitchen there were the broomsticks to make and the cats to feed and new cobwebs to be hung at the castle windows.

As witches go, they weren't really bad, and liked to do someone a good turn when they could.

Not Gribble. She was mean – the meanest witch there ever was.

This morning she was in a rage. She tore round the castle shrieking and screaming until the walls shook. She had lost her tall black pointed hat!

Although the witches hunted high and low for Gribble's hat, they couldn't find it.

The next day when they opened the castle door, they found a large parcel addressed to Gribble. Inside was a brand new black pointed hat. But oh, dear me. It was covered with big pink roses.

Gribble wailed and whined and pulled her hair in a fury. Then suddenly she snatched up the hat and stuck it on her head. She looked into the mirror, and was very surprised at what she saw. A change came over her. First she started to smile. And then she began to dance. She looked so pretty in the tall black pointed hat, with the big pink roses, that she couldn't be mean or cross again.

She gave a party and invited all the wizards, and they danced all night long.

Gribble never took her hat off again!

The Bad-Tempered Giant

A fly tickled the lonely giant's nose. His hands were in the washing-up water so he couldn't brush it away.

It made him very angry. He picked up the washing-up bowl full of giant-sized plates, knives and forks and flung it through the open window. It all landed on the roofs of the houses in the village, sounding like a thunderstorm.

Grannie Griddle had just got back from the shops.

'I've had enough of that giant and his nasty temper,' she thought. 'Last week it was brushes that swept away all our flowers. One day he threw a pillow that burst and we all thought that we were having a snow-storm in August.'

Grannie Griddle went to see Mr Mag, a retired magician. He was pottering about in his garden.

'I have vowed never to use magic on people again,' he told Grannie Griddle. Then he saw a giant fork stuck into his prize marrow.

'But you can still use magic on things,' said the old woman, slyly, and she whispered her plan to Mr Mag.

The poor lonely giant on the hill was in a terrible rage. Everything he owned had turned soft.

He tried to fill his kettle to make some tea but the sponge kettle just soaked up the water. He couldn't even comb his hair with his wobbly comb.

How the villagers laughed when he started to throw everything around. Nothing could hurt them now.

'I expect the magician would make your things normal again if you stopped getting into such paddies,' Grannie Griddle explained to the sad giant. 'Why don't you try helping people for a change?'

So the giant made himself useful, from carrying Grannie Griddle's shopping to chopping down an overgrown bush in Mr Mag's garden.

He made lots of friends by being helpful, and the magician took away the soft spell.

Ho, Hum

Jonathan pressed his nose against the toyshop window and stared longingly at a large, brightly-coloured humming-top. It was gaily painted in bands of red, green and yellow.

Yes, Jonathan knew just what he wanted for his birthday!

But his mother could not afford to buy the big top for him, and she bought him a smaller one instead.

Jonathan was disappointed but did his best not to show it. When he took his new top out to play he tried to pretend that it was not all *that* much smaller than those of his friends. But to make matters worse, he was unable to get his new top to spin. Sadly, Jonathan went back indoors and told his mother about it.

'I expect it's a little stiff,' she said.

'Ho, hum!' sighed Jonathan as he pressed hard down on the knob. 'Ho, hum!'

To his delight, the top began to spin faster and hum louder than any top he had ever seen! When at last it rolled to rest on its side, he eagerly picked it up and pressed down the knob.

Nothing happened!

'Ho, hum!' he sighed once more. And again, the top began to spin and hum! Each time he spoke the magic words, 'Ho, hum!' the top began to spin merrily and hum loudly.

Jonathan ran out to his friends and with a 'Ho, hum!' set his new top spinning and humming faster and louder than all their big ones. His friends were amazed. 'It works like magic!' they cried.

'It *is* magic!' laughed Jonathan. 'Ho, hum! Ho, hum! Ho, hum!'

The Magic Mirror

Sometimes in old tree trunks you can find hollows filled with water. Birds and animals drink at these tiny ponds, and fairies and elves use them. They are also magic mirrors, as one little girl found out.

Kate was usually good. She had a garden to play in in the summer, a playroom when it rained and plenty of friends to play with. But sometimes, just occasionally, she was naughty. One day she was very cross. All of her friends were ill in bed with measles and she had no one to keep her company.

Kate went out into the garden to sulk. She kicked up the gravel from the path, hit at a bumble-bee with a stick and spat at a hollyhock. She even threw a stick at a thrush who was looking for worms in the lawn. Then she sat on an old tree trunk, where a giant tree had once stood, and poked her tongue out at her reflection in the pool of water in the hollow.

What a shock she had! The face that poked out its tongue at her from the pool was old and hideous.

Kate's hair was fair and wavy, but this creature's hair was straight and grey. Kate had pink cheeks and blue eyes, but the reflection in the mirror had purple cheeks and yellow eyes. Kate was wearing a pretty floral dress, but the ugly creature looking at her was clad in a tattered old black cloak. Kate had dainty little fingers, but the old hag in the magic mirror had long claws, with dirt beneath them.

'Oooo!' said Kate.

'That's you,' the magic mirror seemed to say.

'It's not!' protested Kate. 'I don't look like that!'

'You do when you're naughty,' the mirror told her. 'I show you what you are really like, beneath your skin. And that is what you're like when you are cross and sulky.'

'Oh,' said Kate.

Next day when she came out to look into the magic mirror again she saw a fair-haired little girl smiling back at her.

'And that's how I mean to stay,' said Kate.

The Bantam and the Turkey-Cock

Pompous the turkey-cock was king of the farmyard. Don used to watch him from the window of Dumbledor Farm. When any other animal or bird came near, Pompous fluffed out his chest feathers, spread his black and white tail, made all the wattles on his head and neck blush bright red, and strutted about like an emperor.

One day Don's father brought him home a present from the market in a hamper. Don peeped in. There were three small hens and a cock. The hens were brown and yellow, but the cock was bright red, bronze and black, with a red comb.

'They are bantams,' said Don's father. 'Bantams are small hens.'

'We will put them in the yard with the other hens and ducks and turkeys, but they will belong to you,' said Don's mother.

While the bantams were inspecting their new home the turkeys arrived. Pompous at once started strutting. He marched up to the bantams, his face red and his feathers dragging the ground, and he tried to peck them. The bantams looked surprised.

Pompous grew very cross and made a rush at the bantam cock, whose name was Cedric.

'Oh, he'll kill him!' shouted Don.

But Cedric, although he was so small, stood quite still. At the last moment he jumped up and hit the turkey-cock on the chest with his feet. Then he stooped down and ran right between Pompous's legs. As he came out at the back, Cedric turned round and gave the turkey another kick.

The turkey tried attacking Cedric twice more, but each time the same thing happened. The little bantam shot right underneath the big, puffing bird and hit him from behind.

After that, there was a new king of the farmyard. It was Cedric. He used to perch on the yard wall, crowing at the top of his voice every morning. When he heard him crow, Pompous kept out of sight behind the barn.

Look for the other stories about Dumbledor Farm in this book on pages 21, 55 and 93.

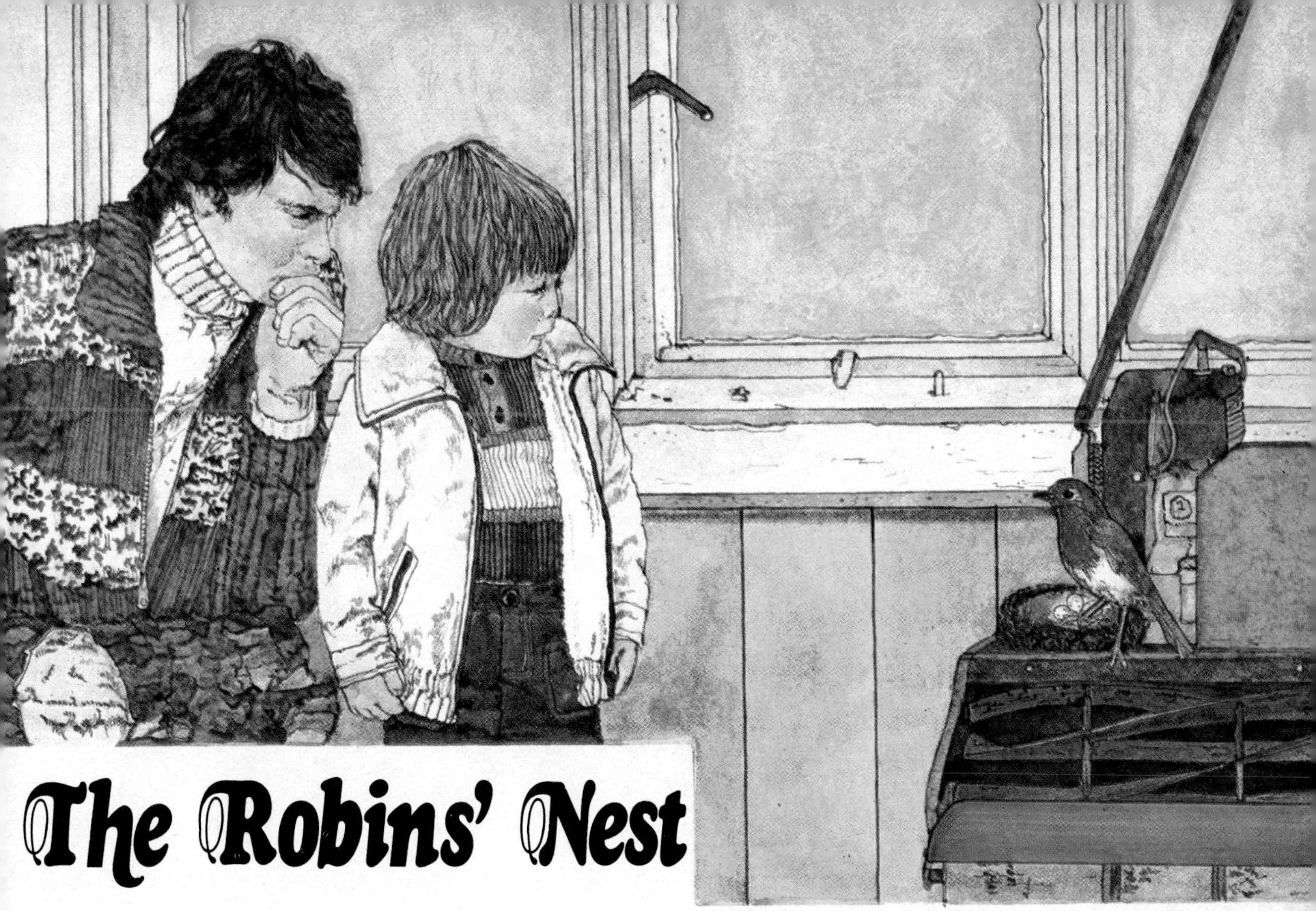

The Robins' Nest

Peter liked to watch the birds at the bird table. From his window he saw them squabble over the bread, nuts and scraps that his mother had piled on the table. There were blackbirds, thrushes, sparrows, chaffinches, starlings, wrens, greenfinches, blue-tits, great tits and woodpeckers. How many of those do you see in your garden?

Peter's favourites were the two robins. They had scarlet breasts and bright eyes, and they were brave little birds, often chasing away others twice as big as themselves. Sometimes they came to the window-sill and looked in at Peter.

'I think they will nest in the garden when spring comes,' said Peter's father. 'We must put up a nesting-box for them.'

He made four nesting-boxes and put them in different parts of the garden so that the robins could choose.

Soon winter was over, and flowers began to appear in the garden. The lawn grew too, and was soon covered with daisies. A pair of blue-tits started building a nest in one of the nest-boxes and some sparrows moved into another, but the other two remained empty.

'I'm sure those robins are nesting somewhere,' said Peter's father, 'but I can't think where. They haven't used the nest-boxes.'

'Never mind about the robins,' said Peter's mother. 'The lawn needs cutting.'

'I'll do it on Saturday afternoon,' promised Peter's father.

But on Saturday afternoon he called Peter to the woodshed, where the lawn-mower was kept.

'Come and see what I've found,' he said.

There on top of the lawn-mower was a little nest of grass and moss. In it were four tiny white eggs with red spots on them. When Peter and his father had finished looking at them, they moved away and soon a robin came and sat on them.

Peter went indoors and told his mother.

'Now I won't be able to mow the lawn until the eggs have hatched and the young birds have flown,' said Peter's father. 'That will be another month.'

'Oh yes you will,' said Peter's mother. 'Our next-door neighbours have a lawn-mower which doesn't have robins in it. Borrow theirs!'

The King's Skis

Everyone in the kingdom of Boz was very cross and miserable, and all because the king of that land had been given a pair of bright red skis for Christmas.

Now when King Merryman was not in bed or having his meals, he was skiing. Dressed in his warmest clothes, he would speed over the snow-covered hills around the palace on his new skis.

'When *are* you going to stop making these dreadful cold spells?' the Queen said to the wizard one day. 'It is almost time for our annual trip to the seaside and it is still snowing!'

'But Your Majesty,' said the wizard, 'I would be only too happy to make a really warm spell and we could *all* go off on holiday, if only the King would stop skiing.'

'Then you must make him stop,' said the Queen, and she hurried off.

So when it was announced later that same day that the King had fallen and broken both his bright red skis, the Queen and all the King's subjects were delighted.

The Queen began to make her holiday plans, and had the royal painters paint the little blue motor-boat for its annual trip to the seaside.

But when everything was ready, the King refused to go. He was now so unhappy because he had broken his beautiful red skis that he would hardly talk to anyone.

The wizard pleaded with King Merryman, but it was no use.

Suddenly the wizard had an idea and hurried off chuckling to himself.

A short time later he returned carrying, of all things – *a pair of bright red skis!*

'New skis!' cried the Queen and the Lord Chamberlain, horrified at the idea.

'These are very special skis,' smiled the wizard, and he whispered something in the King's ear.

'Ho! Ho! Ho!' roared the fat little king. 'You mean I really shall be able to ski on *water*?' he asked the wizard.

So the King and Queen hurried off to the seaside, where the Queen drove the little blue motor-boat, and towed King Merryman across the water on his new red skis.

The Fidget Family's Busy Day

The Fidget family couldn't keep still. They were always doing something, except when they were thinking about what to do next.

Baby Fidget, it was true, did sit in his pram but he was never still, not for a minute! He rattled his rattle and untied his bonnet and sucked his mittens and jiggled his pram till it rocked and swayed.

One day it happened that Mr and Mrs Fidget and their son Phil had all stopped to think what to do next at the same time. They didn't have to think for long, however, because just then they caught sight of the baby rolling out of the gate in his pram. The baby's jiggling had set the pram wheels turning, but he didn't mind a bit.

Mr and Mrs Fidget set off at a great pace and Phil followed behind on his bike, with the cat running behind just for fun. It was unfortunate that the Fidgets lived on a hill, for the pram and baby were now going down it at speed. The Fidgets panted on behind and, reaching the bottom of the hill, turned sharply round a corner in pursuit of their bouncing baby.

On they ran until they came to a field where the local fair was being held. The pram bounced across the ground and rolled up a ramp and on to a roundabout.

'Oh!' cried the Fidgets as they all scrambled on to the roundabout. They went round and round trying to catch the pram, but they all got so giddy that they had to sit down on a nearby dragon. By the time the roundabout had stopped and they had all got off, the pram had bounced on to the rails of a big dipper.

'Oooh!' sighed the crowd at the fairground as the baby went up.

'Aaah!' sighed the Fidgets as the baby came down.

'Oh no!' shouted everyone as the pram came whizzing down for the last time to land right in the middle of the water splash!

Mrs Fidget waded over to the pram and carried the baby home to dry him out. Mr Fidget took the pram home and chopped it up for firewood, while Phil stayed behind and told everyone what had happened.

By the time the Fidgets were all safely back home again they were exhausted. For the first time for as long as any of them could remember they all sat perfectly still and thought about doing – absolutely *nothing at all!*

An Elephant for Christmas

Of all the animals at the zoo Jimmy liked the elephants best. 'I would love an elephant,' he sighed. 'Mummy, do you think I could have just a baby elephant when I'm bigger?'

'I'm afraid not, dear. Baby elephants grow into very big elephants, and where could we keep it?' said Mummy.

It was nearly Christmas time, and Jimmy and his mother went to the big store in the town to buy some presents and to see Father Christmas.

'Mummy,' said Jimmy. 'Father Christmas asked me what I wanted in my stocking.'

'Oh, did he, dear? And what did you say?'

'I said I would like an elephant.'

'Oh, Jimmy, how could you! Whatever did Father Christmas say?'

'Well, he didn't say "No". He just smiled and asked me if there was anything else I wanted. I said, "No thank you. That will be enough".' Mummy sighed and shook her head.

On Christmas morning Jimmy woke very early. It was still dark but the moon was shining through the curtains. He turned over and then sat up wide awake, for standing at the side of his bed was something big and grey. It couldn't be true! It was a baby elephant.

Jimmy put his hand out and stroked it, and when he tried to pick it up, he found underneath a little key. He turned it and an astonishing thing happened. The elephant's trunk began to swing up and down like the elephants at the zoo.

In a moment Jimmy was out of bed.

'Mummy, Daddy,' he shouted. 'There's an elephant by my bed.'

'Oh *really*, Jimmy,' said Daddy. 'It's only five o'clock. Do go back to bed, there's a good chap.'

'But there's ——'

'All right, Jimmy, I'll come and look,' said his mother.

'There, Mummy, by my bed. Isn't it wonderful! And if I turn this key, look! His trunk moves just like a real elephant. I knew Father Christmas wouldn't forget.'

Daniel's Spaniel

Daniel has a spaniel
With great floppy ears,
And Spaniel has a tail
That has been there for years.

Daniel takes him walking
On Sundays I'm told,
Or does Spaniel take Daniel?
For Daniel's two years old.

Brenda Forgets

Brenda Bear yawned and sat up in bed. Then she noticed the corner of the sheet – it had a large knot tied in it.

'Now *why* did I tie that knot?' the little bear asked herself.

She wrinkled her brown, furry brow and thought and thought, but she simply could *not* remember what the knot was supposed to remind her of!

Today was Thursday and Brenda's Aunt Bessie Bear always came to tea every Thursday afternoon.

Back and forth from the pantry to the table hurried the little bear, bringing all sorts of good things.

'But where is the honey?' Brenda said to herself. It wasn't on the table. She looked in the pantry, but there wasn't any honey there either.

'I might just have time to find some before Aunt Bessie arrives,' she thought, glancing at the clock on the mantelpiece.

There was a cold wind blowing and Brenda Bear was glad of her warm, furry coat. Just as she was wondering where to start looking for the honey, she heard a familiar sound. It was a buzzing noise, coming from somewhere above her far up in the clouds.

'How strange,' thought the little bear, 'it's coming from that telegraph pole – at least, it seems to be!'

Although the wind tugged at her coat, she began to climb the pole. When she was half-way up, she heard a shout from below.

'Whatever are you doing up that pole, Brenda Bear?'

Brenda looked down and there was her Aunt Bessie Bear looking up at her.

'I am looking for honey,' replied Brenda.

Aunt Bessie held up a jar of golden honey. 'I told you not to forget I was bringing the honey today,' she called.

As soon as Brenda saw the honey she came hurrying down the pole.

'So *that* is why I tied the knot in my sheet,' she smiled.

'What made you think you would find honey at the top of the telegraph pole?' asked her aunt.

'Well,' said Brenda, looking puzzled, 'I could hear the bees buzzing up there and I thought . . .'

Aunt Bessie did not let the little bear finish. 'Oh Brenda, you are a little silly,' she laughed. 'The buzzing you heard is the wind blowing through the telegraph wires.'

'It did seem a funny place to look for honey!' agreed Brenda, as she and her aunt hurried home to tea.

Monty Mouse

'Where *did* I put that key?' cried Monty Mouse in dismay. He had looked in all the pockets of his blue coat, but he could not find the key to his front door. He began to feel rather silly standing outside, and then it started to rain.

All the windows of his tiny round house were shut tight. He peeped through the kitchen window, and there was the key lying on the kitchen table!

Just at that moment, along came Mr Policeman Bunny. 'Hello, Monty. What are you doing out there in the rain?' he said.

'I-I-I've b-been to the shops and I f-f-forgot my key,' stammered Monty. 'I am such a forgetful fellow. I have left it on the kitchen table.'

'Well now, let me see!' said Policeman Bunny, stroking his chin. 'I know,' he went on, 'I will break one of the windows and then I will climb in and get the key. Then I'll open the door for you.'

'Yes . . . but I painted all the windows yesterday and I don't think the paint is dry yet,' replied Monty.

'Well, it's the only way, Monty,' replied Policeman Bunny, and he gave the window a bang with his truncheon. As he was about to jump on to the kitchen floor, Monty suddenly remembered he had forgotten to remove the tin of bright blue paint which was on the floor.

'Oh! Do be careful, Mr Bunny!' shouted Monty, but he was too late. Mr Bunny's boot went right into the tin, and the blue paint went all over his trousers.

Now this made Policeman Bunny *very* angry. He picked up the key from the kitchen table and opened the door to a very wet and sad Monty on the step.

'I don't know how much Mrs Tubwash will charge to clean all this, but you will have to pay, Monty!' he cried.

'Oh!' sighed Monty, 'I've only a few pennies in my money-box, and that's not enough to pay Mrs Tubwash. I shall have to get a job. I wonder if Mr Hare would help me? I could deliver his morning papers. I still have my old bicycle in the garden shed.'

'Yes, I think I can give you a job, Monty,' said Mr Hare, when Monty had told him his story.

Soon Monty had enough money to pay Mrs Tubwash, but he still has his morning paper round, and when he hurries off each day, he always remembers his key.

The King's Rocket

'We never do anything exciting and new,' complained the King. 'We must do something to make our country famous all round the wide world.'

Then the King jumped to his feet. 'We will build a rocket and go to the moon!' he cried.

So it was settled, and the court inventor was ordered to build the rocket. He had never made a rocket before but promised to do his best.

He worked very hard, and the day came when the completed rocket was standing upright on the palace lawn.

The King was delighted. 'Why, it is perfect! That will get me to the moon in no time at all.'

The inventor was a little alarmed at this. 'I did not know that you were going to pilot the rocket,' he said.

'Of course!' cried the King. 'It is the sort of job only a king can do. Besides,' he added, 'I want to be the first to taste the cheese!'

This was another surprise for the inventor. 'Cheese?' he asked the King.

'Yes, cheese,' replied the King. 'The moon is made of green cheese. Everybody knows that.'

The King was climbing aboard the rocket when he suddenly asked the inventor, 'Are you quite sure the engine is powerful enough to carry me all the way to the moon?'

Now as it happened, the inventor had not been exactly sure how to make the engine, and had finally used eight fifty-pence rockets which had somehow been left over from the last firework display. 'You will be all right,' he said hopefully.

Then the rocket roared into life.

For a little way it went straight upwards. Then suddenly it shot round the back of the palace and crashed right through the roof of the royal dairy. The King was thrown into a large vat of soft cheese.

'Cheese!' he cried. 'The moon *is* made of cheese, just as I said!'

Poor old King. He soon realised he was only in the royal dairy. 'Never mind,' he said, 'this is fine cheese. Perhaps our country can become famous for its cheese.' And it did!

The Little Red Yacht

There was once a little red yacht. He had a tall red mast, and fine white sails and beautiful pointed bows. And he loved to race with the other little yachts down the stream.

'I am going to win today,' he would say, but he never did, because he always found something interesting to watch on the way. Then, instead of sailing swift and sure, he would spin round in the middle of the stream, or bump his bows into the bank.

'Silly little red yacht!' jeered the others. 'He will never win a race.'

'Oh, yes I could!' snapped the little red yacht. 'I would have won today, only I was watching the ducklings learning to swim.'

The little red yacht's best friend was a little black duckling, and sometimes they would go for a sail-swim together.

Then, one day, the little black duckling was nowhere to be seen.

'I do hope he has not swum down the stream,' cried Mother Duck, flapping her wings in alarm. 'Round the far bend is a waterfall. A little duckling would certainly be drowned if he fell over the edge.'

'I will sail after him!' cried the little red yacht bravely, and at once he let the wind fill his fine sails and off he went.

He sailed swiftly round the long bend of the stream, and there he met the other yachts.

'Have you seen the little black duckling?' he called.

'No,' said the other yachts. 'We're having a race. Hi, wait for us!'

But the little red yacht took no notice. Swift and sure, he sailed in and out between them. One, two, three yachts were left behind. Four yachts! The little red yacht was out in front. His beautiful bows rose over the wavelets. And at last, there was little black duckling ahead, getting dreadfully close to the waterfall.

Just in time the little red yacht sailed in front of him. He shook his sails and said, 'Shoo, go home! Go home, little black duckling, before it is too late!'

So the little black duckling went safely home and the little red yacht won the race!

Hubert's Helping Hand

When Hubert the hedgehog found the note on his doorstep, he was very puzzled. It had only two words on it:

HELP PLEASE?

But it didn't say who wanted help or what sort of help they wanted. Hubert was a very helpful hedgehog, and so without waiting to eat his breakfast he set off across the field.

First he called at Mrs Badger's house. But Mrs Badger was much too busy to talk to him.

'I have cakes to make for the party,' she said, and shut the door.

Hubert went on a little way and met Mr and Mrs Rabbit, with all their children.

'Can't stop now,' said Mr Rabbit. 'We have to get ready for the party.'

Hubert was hot and a little bit hungry. He wished that he had stopped for breakfast. He thought that he would ask the owl. He would know who needed help. But Owl shook his head.

'I don't know of anyone needing help,' he hooted. 'Why don't you come to the party?'

But Hubert hadn't been invited.

The owl flew off and Hubert sat for a few minutes under the tree. It seemed no one wanted his help after all, and everyone was going to the party except him.

He was hungry and disappointed as he turned back for home.

He had just opened his front door when Mrs Duck came running up behind him.

'Please wait,' she cried. 'I so badly need your help.'

She was quite out of breath and sat down on Hubert's doorstep. 'I left you a note,' she panted.

'Oh,' said Hubert. 'So it's you I've been looking for?'

He showed Mrs Duck the note, and she began to laugh.

'Dearie me,' she cried, 'the wind must have torn it in half.'

And there was the other half, caught on the branch of the tree!

Hubert spread both the pieces out on the ground. They said:

FROM MRS DUCK
TO MR HEDGEHOG.
I AM HAVING A PARTY.
CAN YOU
COME AND
HELP PLEASE?

When they had stopped laughing, Mrs Duck took Hubert to the party where he helped to set the tables with food.

And then he had an *enormous* breakfast.

Pirates in the Garden Pond

It was Sunday evening. Wind and rain beat on the house. Tommy put down his pirate book and lay back in bed.

'Ho, hum, school tomorrow,' he sighed. 'I'd rather be on a pirate ship!'

More rain fell. It pounded on the roof. It splashed in the garden pond.

Tommy slept. He slept so heavily he didn't hear a great *plop* as something landed in the pond.

Next morning was sunny. Tommy awoke to hear strange sounds coming through his window – the creak of ropes, the flap of sails and the sound of water against a ship's side.

Then a salty voice shouted, 'Ahoy, matey, get out of bed! Come aboard!'

Tommy looked out. A pirate ship lay at anchor in the pond. A black flag fluttered from a mast-head. Sunburned men with handkerchiefs around their heads stood on the main deck. They waved to Tommy.

The captain stood on the highest deck which was level with Tommy's window. 'Avast, swabs,' the captain shouted. 'Run out the gangplank. Matey's coming aboard.'

The crew pushed a board to the window and Tommy walked carefully across.

The captain led Tommy to his cabin. Treasure maps lay on his desk, an iron chest stood in the corner and weapons hung on the walls.

Tommy and the captain sat in the cabin all day and talked of pirate things till sunset.

Then Tommy walked back over the gangplank. As he crawled into bed he sighed, 'Father'll be surprised tomorrow!'

Tommy slept heavily. He didn't hear the wind and rain begin again. He didn't hear a great *whoosh* as something lifted out of the pond and sailed away.

Next morning was clear. Tommy jumped out of bed and ran into his father's room.

'I'm sorry I missed school on Monday,' he cried. 'I was on a pirate ship. It's in the garden pond.'

Father looked out of his window. 'There's nothing there, Tommy. And you didn't miss school. Today *is* Monday. You just read too many exciting pirate stories too late in the evening, matey!'

Scissors and Pins

'That's enough for today McAlistair,' said Miss Hemstitch to her parrot. Her rheumatism grew painful when she sat too long. She was making a dress for Miss Pimble who was very particular and wanted her dress by Saturday.

Miss Hemstitch stumbled as she got up, and over went her pin box.

'Dearie me!' squawked McAlistair, for the pins lay in hundreds all over the floor. Some sparkled in the lamplight. Others hid in the shadows.

'My scissors are blunt and I am tired. Now my pins need picking up,' said Miss Hemstitch sadly.

As she climbed up to bed the moon climbed slowly up the sky. He loved to peep in at people's windows. Through her lace curtains he saw Miss Pimble snoring on her embroidered pillows. Then he sent a moonbeam into Miss Hemstitch's living room. What was that twinkling?

McAlistair blinked. 'Scissors and pins!' he croaked, and the moon saw the pins.

Upstairs he peeped in on Miss Hemstitch under her patchwork quilt.

'Scissors and pins,' she murmured.

The moon wasted no time. In his tiny cottage Sam Snickett, the knife-grinder, was dozing in his chair. The moon shone in on his grindstone and twinkled along his bench of scythes, scissors and knives. Then he danced around old Sam till the pair of scissors he was holding sparkled like a star. Sam smiled and nodded.

Next morning Miss Hemstitch got up early. She sighed to think of the work waiting for her. What was that on the doormat? A pair of scissors!

But another surprise was waiting. As McAlistair gave a shriek of joy, Miss Hemstitch dropped the scissors, and when she picked them up they were covered with clinging pins! The scissors were like a magnet, and in no time at all she had used them to collect every single pin.

'Thank you, McAlistair,' said Miss Hemstitch. 'You made me drop my scissors.'

Miss Pimble got her new dress, and Sam Snickett took the old scissors in exchange for the marvellous magnetic pair.

Poor King Fuzziwig

Little Witch Silverlocks stood in the great throne room of the palace looking very small and miserable. Before her strutted the King trying to look important, but only appearing rather foolish.

'I have nothing against witches,' he said, 'but . . . well, nowadays' . . . and he wiped his face with his handkerchief, 'well, they are rather out-of-date, and such an expense.'

He stopped, and then said quickly, 'There is a nice cottage in the country for you, so off you go with your cat and live quietly.'

But soon things began to happen that King Fuzziwig had not thought about.

First it was the mice.

Now that Tompkin, the witch's cat, had gone, they scampered gleefully all over the palace, and ate the King's dinner before his very eyes.

'Mercy on us!' screeched Fuzziwig. 'Who is responsible for this?'

'Well, Tompkin used to catch mice,' explained the butler, lifting one out of the soup. 'The other cats cannot do it half so well. We shall have to put down poison and traps.'

That cost the King a lot of money.

Then it was the servants. They would not dust and sweep the palace.

'What is the matter with them?' stormed Fuzziwig.

'Well,' explained the Queen, 'you see, the witch's broomstick used to do all the work while the servants did the cooking. We shall have to get more servants.'

That cost more money still.

One day there was a panic in the palace. The green dragon had come back. Years ago the dragon had appeared on the mountainside looking for food. The witch had soon chased him away, but now she had gone.

'Call out the army,' screamed the terrified King as everybody ran away.

'But there is no money to pay the army,' said the Lord Chamberlain.

'I was a fool to send the witch away,' groaned the poor King.

'Do not despair,' said a voice, and the King turned to see the witch by his side. 'I heard about the dragon and flew here on my broomstick at once. When I have got rid of it may I come back? I think you need me after all.'

'Need you? We cannot manage without you,' said the King, with relief. 'Do not ever go away again.'

So she never did.

Lionel's Walk

Once upon a time there was a cat who wanted to be the very first cat to walk round the world.

'Please let me go,' said Lionel to his mother. He pleaded and pleaded until in the end she said, 'I suppose if you must, you must, but I cannot let you go alone. I will walk with you.' So they set off together.

'Where are you going?' asked a ginger cat, who was a friend of Lionel's mother.

'We are walking round the world,' said Lionel proudly.

'We're not, really,' whispered Lionel's mother to her friend. 'I'm pretending to go with him, so that I can see he comes to no harm on the way.'

'I understand,' whispered Ginger. Then she said loudly, so that Lionel could hear, 'I'll go along too, to keep you company.'

Lionel was not very pleased, but there was nothing he could do about it.

'Which way is the right way then?' asked Ginger, winking at Lionel's mother.

'Through the park first,' said Lionel, to give himself time to plan a route.

Unfortunately, there were lots of Lionel's friends about that day. By the time they reached the gates on the far side of the park, nineteen cats had decided to walk round the world with him.

Suddenly Lionel was not so sure that his idea was a good one. He did not really know the way, and anyway he was beginning to feel hungry.

'I wonder how Lionel will explain himself out of this,' whispered his mother to Ginger.

Lionel was still trying to think of a reason for going home, when it began to rain. He stopped and turned to face the other cats.

'You will all agree, I'm sure,' he said, that we cannot walk round the world in the rain. Everyone turn about and go home as fast as you can.'

Ginger and Lionel's mother sat under a hedge and waited for the rain to stop.

'I suppose Lionel will grow up one day,' sighed his mother, as she watched him disappear in the direction of home.

'Of course he will,' said Ginger wisely. 'Cats always do.'

Three Brave Friends

Peter the Pixie was the first to find out that the giant was in a temper. He was sitting quietly fishing beside the giant's stream. Then he heard a roaring sound and the giant appeared.

'How dare you fish there!' shouted the giant. 'Go away!' Poor Peter ran off in a great fright.

The next day, Peter's brother Paul was gathering sticks in the wood and the same thing happened. The giant roared at him too and Paul hurried away.

The pixies decided to hold a council of war. Winter was coming and they needed wood for their fires. They also needed to catch plenty of fish, which they dried to eat when food was scarce.

'We must go and ask the giant what we have done to make him so cross,' said one old pixie.

But all the pixies were frightened and nobody wanted to do it. At last, Peter and Paul said they would go, although they did not feel very brave.

So the two brothers set off to see the giant. As they came near the giant's palace, they met his favourite cat, Max.

'What is the matter with the giant?' asked Paul. 'He used to be so kind.'

'He has a thorn in his foot,' said Max. 'He will not let anybody touch it, but it hurts him every time he moves.'

'Help us get into the palace,' said Peter, 'and we will get it out.'

When it was dark, Max led them through the kitchens and up into the giant's bedroom. The room shook with the giant's groans. His foot was hanging out of bed and Peter and Paul could see the huge thorn in it.

The three friends held on to each other, and Paul in front gave a mighty tug on the thorn. The giant awoke with a shriek, and the cat and the pixies landed in a heap on the floor. The giant jumped out of bed in a worse rage than ever. He picked up the pixies in one hand, but as they both struggled the giant saw the thorn lying on the floor.

'Oh!' he said. 'I can walk again and it doesn't hurt.' A smile spread over his face and he put the two pixies gently on the floor at his feet.

After that the giant gave his cat, Max, and the two pixies many presents, but best of all, he let the pixie folk fish in his stream and collect sticks in his wood for ever.

Mr Pepper's Marrow

Mr Pepper looked at his giant marrow with dismay. Only yesterday the marrow had sat there large and healthy and now it had almost withered away.

Mr Pepper sat down and cried.

'Oh, do stop crying. I forgot my umbrella and your tears are making me quite wet,' said a cross voice.

Mr Pepper looked down and saw a field-mouse squeezing water from her dress.

'I'm sorry,' he said. 'It's just that this year I was so sure I'd win first prize with my marrow. Every year it's the same. I grow a beautiful large marrow and then just before the show the poor thing dies. My neighbour, Mr Snodgrass, always wins the prize and his marrows are never as fine as mine.'

'I know why you never win a prize,' said the field-mouse. 'I was coming out of my hole the other night when I saw Mr Snodgrass stick a pin into your marrow. But never mind,' she continued, 'I have a very good friend who may be able to help you. Do you have any more marrows?'

'Only a small one,' replied Mr Pepper, and he showed the field-mouse a tiny marrow no bigger than a cucumber.

'Cheer up, you may win the prize yet,' said the field-mouse mysteriously, as she hurried off to find her friend, who happened to be the weatherman.

The field-mouse found the weatherman in his castle in a wood.

'How can I help you?' said the weatherman, and he sat and listened to the field-mouse's story.

'Well, that's quite easy,' said the weatherman, when the field-mouse had finished, 'I shall arrange for a hot sun to shine for the three days before the show. Mr Pepper's tiny marrow will grow until it is bigger than the first one. Mr Snodgrass's marrows will all become over-ripe and burst,' and he smiled as he said good-bye.

The field-mouse hurried back to Mr Pepper's garden. Sure enough the sun shone hotter than ever before, and Mr Pepper's marrow grew bigger and bigger as the days went by.

They heard shrieks of rage from next door as pips from the burst marrows hit Mr Snodgrass.

Mr Pepper was delighted with his marrow and most grateful to his new friend. He gave her a meal, and told her she was welcome to come and live in his garden.

Of course, Mr Pepper's marrow won first prize for the largest in the show. Nobody had ever seen such a wonderful marrow before.

As for Mr Snodgrass, he was so ashamed that he moved away and was never seen in the village again.

Oswald Owl

The very day Oswald Owl learned to fly he decided to leave the nest in the old barn roof.

'Now I can fly,' he hooted confidently, 'I will be quite able to look after myself.'

Mr and Mrs Owl were not quite so sure Oswald was right, but he was so determined to leave home that they found him a house of his own, in a hollow tree.

Oswald was delighted with his new home. When night-time came, he tucked himself up in bed and settled down to sleep. An hour later he was still wide awake.

He could *not* get to sleep.

'The wood is full of little animals,' he thought. 'I'm sure to find someone awake to talk to.'

So he got out of bed and started flying through the quiet wood. First he knocked on Mr and Mrs Rabbit's door.

'I can't get to sleep,' he hooted. 'Please will you come and play with me?'

'At this time of night! I've never heard of such a thing,' screamed Mr Rabbit crossly. And he slammed the door.

Soon he was knocking on the door of Mr Miner Mole.

'Please let me in Mr Mole,' cried Oswald. 'I'm cold and I can't get to sleep.' But Mr Miner Mole was so busy digging a new tunnel that he did not hear him.

Then he tried Fisherman Frog, Marmaduke Mouse and the Blackbird family, but they were all fast asleep.

Poor Oswald felt that he was the only one in the world who was not asleep.

He sat on a branch and looked over the dark wood. Then he saw something that frightened him very much indeed. Staring at him, from the tree opposite, were four enormous golden eyes. They began to move towards him.

'Hullo, Oswald,' said Mr Owl, as he settled on the branch beside him.

'Good evening, Oswald,' said Mrs Owl. 'Are you having a pleasant night?'

'Oh, dear,' sighed Oswald. 'Everyone else is asleep except me – and you too,' he added, looking puzzled.

And Mr and Mrs Owl laughed and laughed. Oswald could not think why.

'You see, Oswald,' said Mr Owl, when he had stopped laughing, 'owls never sleep at night when they are old enough to leave home. I thought you knew that.'

Oswald did feel silly.

'Never mind,' said Mr and Mrs Owl, 'all young owls make mistakes. It is only very old owls that are wise.'

The Special Party

Billie and Bob, the toy rabbits, were painting their house.

'It's looking nice,' said Billie. 'When it's finished, we'll ask our friends to see it, and have a party.'

'Party!' gasped Bob. 'That reminds me – it's Sailor Doll's party today. We're supposed to go. It starts at three o'clock.'

Billie peeped under a dust sheet at the clock.

'It's nearly three now,' he said. 'We must change out of these paint-covered jumpers and overalls. But first find the invitation, because there was something special about the party, and I can't remember what it is.'

They dived under the dust sheets, but it was difficult to find anything because the furniture was in a muddle.

The rabbits were so busy that Tim, the toy soldier, had to knock twice before he was heard.

'Hurry up,' said Tim. 'I've driven round Toyland in my toy car collecting the toys who are going to the party. Toy Dog and Fluffy Kitten are waiting in the car.'

'We can't go in these painting clothes!' cried Bob.

'We haven't time to change,' said Billie. 'Tim and the others are waiting, and we can't make them late. We must go as we are!'

Billie and Bob put on their overcoats and joined Tim and the others in the car. Soon they arrived at Sailor Doll's house.

Billie and Bob were surprised that Sailor Doll was not wearing his sailor uniform, but dressed as a clown. When Tim took off his coat, they saw that instead of his soldier uniform, Tim had on a cook's apron. Toy Poodle and Fluffy Kitten took off their coats, and Billie and Bob saw that Toy Poodle had on a ballet skirt, and Fluffy Kitten had on a tiger suit.

'I knew there was something special about this party!' said Bob. 'I remember now that the invitation said "Fancy Dress Party"!'

Sailor Doll said, 'How clever of you rabbits to think of coming as painters! You look jolly in your paint-covered jumpers and overalls.'

Billie and Bob just laughed and laughed.

The Wedding of Mrs Fox

One day a wolf went to call on Mrs Fox. He knocked at the door. The cat, who was Mrs Fox's maid, opened it.

'Good morning, Mrs Cat,' said the wolf. 'Is Mrs Fox at home?'

'She is in mourning, sir,' replied the cat. 'Old Mr Fox died the other day and she is heart-broken and will see no one.'

'Will she marry me?' asked the wolf.

'I'll ask her, sir,' said the cat, and she ran upstairs swishing her long tail. She knocked on Mrs Fox's bedroom door. 'There is a gentleman below who wants to know if you will marry him,' she said.

'Has he red stockings on, and does he have a pointed nose?' asked Mrs Fox.

'No,' replied the cat.

'Then he's no use to me,' said Mrs Fox.

The wolf went sadly away. Then a dog, a deer, a hare, a lion, a bear, and many other animals came to Mrs Fox's door, but they were all sent away because they did not wear red stockings or have a pointed nose.

At last a young fox came to the door. 'Has the gentleman red stockings and a pointed nose?' asked Mrs Fox.

'Yes,' replied the cat, 'he has.'

'Then show him upstairs,' said Mrs Fox, 'for he shall be my new husband.'

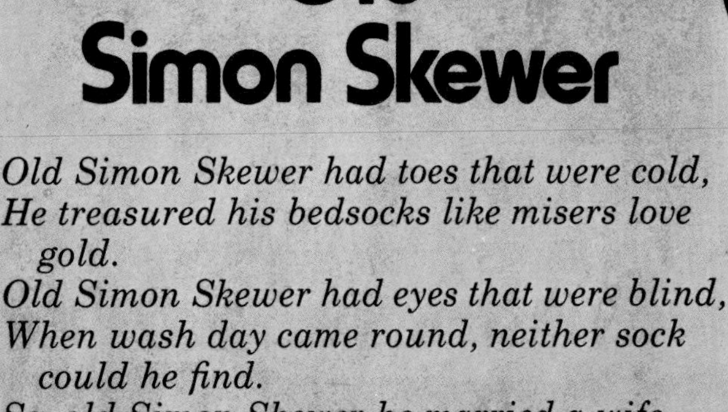

Old Simon Skewer

Old Simon Skewer had toes that were cold,
He treasured his bedsocks like misers love gold.
Old Simon Skewer had eyes that were blind,
When wash day came round, neither sock could he find.
So, old Simon Skewer he married a wife,
(She'd suffered from cold feet the whole of her life).
And now, when they both go to bed every night,
She wears the left sock and he wears the right!

To Train